Psychosis

Stories of Recovery and Hope

Note

Health and social care practice and knowledge are constantly changing and developing as new research and treatments, changes in procedures, drugs and equipment become available.

The authors, editor and publishers have, as far as is possible, taken care to confirm that the information complies with the latest standards of practice and legislation.

Psychosis

Stories of Recovery and Hope

Hannah Cordle
Jane Fradgley
Dr Jerome Carson
Dr Frank Holloway
Paul Richards

QUAY
BOOKS

A division of MA Healthcare Ltd

Quay Books Division, MA Healthcare Ltd, St Jude's Church, Dulwich Road, London SE24 0PB

British Library Cataloguing-in-Publication Data
A catalogue record is available for this book

© MA Healthcare Limited 2011

ISBN-10: 1 85642 4200
ISBN-13: 978 1 85642 4202

Printed by CLE, Huntingdon, Cambridgeshire

Table of Contents

GUY'S &
St THOMAS' CHARITY

Guy's and St Thomas' Charity

Guy's and St Thomas' Charity is delighted to have supported this inspiring collection of personal narratives, highlighting the many different symptoms and roads to recovery experienced by people with psychosis.

The Charity has a track record of supporting initiatives to promote a better understanding of psychosis and encouraging early diagnosis, as well as more effective treatment and recovery. It is also keen to tackle the stigma and taboo associated with mental ill-health, through academic studies and training for professionals, as well as arts projects which challenge common misconceptions around the syndrome in the wider community.

Guy's and St Thomas' Charity supports initiatives that enable innovation, creativity and learning in the NHS, with a particular focus on improving health and wellbeing in Lambeth and Southwark. The Charity supports a wide range of activities and services to improve clinical care, pioneering innovations in diagnosis and the prevention of ill health. Cutting-edge research is brought together with the insights of staff working on the 'frontline' to better understand particular diseases and disorders and to test new approaches towards delivering services. An improved clinical outcome as well as a better experience for patients is at the heart of the Charity's ethos.

The Charity's history goes back many centuries to the re-establishment of St Thomas' Hospital by Edward VI following the Reformation in 1553 and the building of Guy's Hospital by Thomas Guy in 1721. The careful management of the Charity's funds and assets, together with ongoing donations and legacies, continue to enrich the work of the hospitals and associated healthcare organisations today.

Further details about the Charity's work can be found at:
www.gsttcharity.org.uk

Biographies

Hannah Cordle is an assistant psychologist for South London and Maudsley NHS Foundation Trust. She previously worked for ten years in journalism and public relations before completing a postgraduate diploma in psychology.

Jane Fradgley studied fashion design and worked as a designer for many years. More recently Jane has been developing her skills as a photographer and has exhibited her work in galleries around London and the South of England. Her portraits have appeared in several mental health journals. Working in the voluntary sector, Jane assists in facilitating art groups for vulnerable adults.

Dr Jerome Carson is a consultant clinical psychologist. Jerome works in a community mental health team in South West Lambeth, part of the South London and Maudsley NHS Foundation Trust. Since 2006, he has been wrestling with the concept of recovery and has been involved in a number of local initiatives. In addition Jerome is currently inspired by the concepts of positive psychology and wellbeing, though appreciates the difficulty of applying some of these ideas with people with more long term mental health problems.

Dr Frank Holloway has worked as a psychiatrist since 1979. He trained at Kings College Hospital, London and became a Consultant Adult Psychiatrist in 1987. He has been involved in the closure of a large mental hospital and in the development of innovative community-based mental health services in South London. He is a former Chair of the Faculty of Rehabilitation and Social Psychiatry of the Royal College of Psychiatrists. His research interests include psychiatric rehabilitation, psychiatric ethics, mental health law and how mental health services work. He is an Honorary Senior Lecturer in the Health Services and Population Research Department of the Institute of Psychiatry.

Paul Richards is manager of the print department at Southside Rehabilitation Association (SRA) Ltd, a charity in West Norwood that provides employment training to people with mental health problems. He has over 40 years experience of design, printing and layout, most recently specialising in publications relating to mental health.

Chapter 1

Introduction - Understanding the Journey
Hannah Cordle

The seeds of this project grew out of two recovery initiatives which took place at the South West Sector Community Mental Health Team in Streatham between 2008 and 2010. Firstly, Dr Jerome Carson and six service users produced a series of papers entitled *Recovery Heroes* on individuals whose journeys of recovery from mental illness could inspire other service users and professionals alike (Sen et al, 2009). Secondly, Jane Fradgley led the *Photographing Hope* project where six service users attempted to define their own meaning of the word 'hope' by taking and exhibiting a series of inspiring digital photographs. These projects used a unique partnership model between service users and mental health professionals which enabled people to take a lead role in their own recovery. I was fortunate enough to work on both projects which, thanks to the commitment of our service users, Dr Carson's enthusiasm and Jane Fradgley's artistic vision, were a great success.

During this time it became clear that there was scope for a larger piece of work that would develop some of the themes around recovery and hope that we had touched upon. These included identifying real-life role models for people with mental illness; demonstrating that recovery is a real possibility; and promoting hope as an important factor in recovery. Another significant issue was the need to raise the profile of recovery from psychosis in a similar way as has happened with bipolar disorder in recent years. The reason for this was encapsulated by one of the contributors to this book, consultant psychiatrist Dr Glenn Roberts, the lead on recovery for the Royal College of Psychiatrists, who said, "People with bipolar disorder often seem accepting or even helped by their diagnosis, join organisations like the Manic Depression Fellowship, read *Pendulum* magazine, are often positive about their medications, set up self-management groups or even whole approaches and often appear as contributors, colleagues and leaders in recovery contexts. Not so people with a schizophrenia diagnosis… who are underrepresented in collections of recovery stories or as collaborative leaders in recovery contexts," (Roberts, 2010). The need to create psychosis recovery heroes is justified within the pages of this book, with only one person naming economist and Nobel laureate John Nash as an exemplar of recovery from schizophrenia. Although his story, depicted in the film *A Beautiful Mind*, is inspiring it could be seen as distant and unobtainable to many ordinary people. So Dr Carson conceived the idea for *Psychosis: Stories of Recovery and Hope*, with the aim of showing that there are many positive, inspiring and untold stories of people not just coping with schizophrenia and related disorders, but who are also making valued and valuable contributions to society. We were successful in securing the support of Guy's and St Thomas' Charity, an organisation which has done such a huge amount to promote mental health in South London, including funding our own *Photographing Hope* project. Dr Carson was to be the lead clinical consultant with Jane Fradgley as the main photographer and artistic director. The expertise and assistance of consultant psychiatrist Dr Frank Holloway, former clinical director of Croydon Integrated Adult Mental Health Services, and designer Paul Richards of the South London-based mental health charity SRA Ltd, was also enlisted. My task, as a former journalist now working as an assistant psychologist, was to work closely with each of the 14 contributors to produce the narratives that would form the backbone of the book.

This process involved conducting a two hour long semi-structured interview, either in person or on the telephone, with each contributor. The interviews followed a standard format, beginning with a brief introduction of the person's background; a description of their transition into psychosis and experiences of the mental health system; and ending with their thoughts on recovery and hope. This format was chosen because I felt it was important to strike a balance between allowing the contributors – some of whom had patchy and impressionistic recollections of their own experiences – the freedom to tell their story in their own way while producing a reader-friendly result. It would also achieve the aim of making the text as clear and accessible as possible for our most important target audiences, readers with psychosis and their carers. Each narrative was then written up using the same structure to ensure a consistency of style across the book. The interviews were designed to draw out but not exaggerate the clinical aspects of having psychosis such as symptoms, medication or hospitalisation in each narrative. The reason for this, also identified by Dr Glenn Roberts (see his chapter in this book), was to avoid dehumanising the individual and reducing them to a diagnosis. It was equally important to include information on the individual's process of recovery and their understanding of the concept of hope, which to my mind could be more beneficial to others who were seeking recovery themselves.

There was very little editorial interference needed from me in the crafting of these narratives. Indeed, in some chapters, large sections of the text are almost direct reproductions of the interviews themselves. Where this was not the case, I needed simply to join the dots rather than paint an entire landscape. Although I have a background as a reporter, I deliberately avoided using the journalistic technique of looking for the sound bite, hook or angle to each story. These stories do not necessarily have the traditional beginning, middle or end but were allowed to flow naturally from the individual and take on a life of their own. This aimed to reflect how recovery is a work in progress rather than a finished product for many people (Ward, 2009).

Some of the contributors were experienced in telling their stories, while others were not, yet all described them better than any third party could have done. Perhaps recounting the story orally to a trained writer, rather than trying to write it down themselves, facilitated this process. The resulting narratives are a tribute to, in the words of Bose Dania (see her chapter in this book), the contributors' understanding of the journey which in itself is a signifier of recovery. Each contributor has something original and practical to say on recovery, be it the importance of spirituality, getting a job or maintaining their personal appearance, which can offer us new directions in the recovery debate. The narratives are complemented by Jane Fradgley's powerful black and white portraits, which capture the dignity and individuality of each contributor.

During the editorial process, I was struck by the willingness, openness and enthusiasm of each contributor to tell his or her story. This was despite the potential distress that could be experienced by recounting and reading back a story of, in some cases, a lifetime dominated by severe mental illness. The bravery this entailed was brought home when one contributor told me that he had to mentally prepare himself before reading back the first draft. But when I asked the contributors for some evaluative feedback, the beneficial value of telling and rereading their own narrative also became clear. Some were surprised at how confident and open they appear in the text; others found it a useful benchmark of their own recovery; one contributor hoped her story would help others with mental illness by raising awareness and charitable funds. The process demonstrated the importance of narrative and showed how it could successfully be developed in future as a therapeutic intervention, even led by writers and journalists rather than psychiatrists or psychologists. It also revealed a hunger from the service users themselves for more opportunity to produce narrative, with several contributors seeking to take the work further through either publishing their own memoirs or developing other autobiographical projects.

Psychosis: Stories of Recovery and Hope includes chapters from leading clinicians in the area of recovery. In *What is Psychosis?* Dr Frank Holloway provides an overview of psychosis from a clinical perspective that includes a description of definitions, diagnoses and treatments of the condition. In *Recovery: The Long and Winding Road That Leads...?* Dr Jerome Carson surveys the recovery landscape and provides examples of recovery in practice at both an individual and group level. In his chapter *Recovery and Personal Narratives,* Dr Glenn Roberts outlines the importance of stories at the individual level and to the recovery movement as a whole. The *Afterword: The value of recovery stories.* sees myself, Dr Holloway and Dr Carson reflecting on how each of the narratives in this book are living examples of recovery in action according to four significant indicators defined by leading academics in the field.

Thanks must first go to the 14 contributors to the book who so openly shared their stories and made producing it so straightforward and enjoyable. This book is dedicated to them and the other people who have been, are and will be diagnosed with psychosis in the United Kingdom, in the anticipation that it will inspire recovery and generate hope. Thank you to the Trustees of Guy's and St Thomas's Charity who supported our vision and made this project possible. To my co editors Dr Frank Holloway, Jane Fradgley and Paul Richards, thank you for your advice and assistance throughout the completion of the project. Special thanks to Dr Carson for giving me the opportunity to work on this and many other fascinating and valuable projects. I also thank the many others who assisted me including Anant Chander, Sam Holmes, Mary O'Connor, Alita Howe, Kate Mensah, Ameena Sameja, Tosin Arogundade, Sandy Flowerday and Thu Nguyen of Quay Books. Finally, many thanks to Ben for all his support throughout an unforgettable year.

References

Dania, B (2008) *Understanding the Journey*. Unpublished manuscript

Roberts, G (2010) Personal email communication with Dr Jerome Carson

Sen, D, Morgan, S and Carson, J (2009) Recovery heroes: A profile of Dolly Sen. *A Life in the Day*, **13**, (2), 6-8

Ward, M (2009) *My recovery: A work in progress*. Presentation at the Lambeth Recover Me conference.

Chapter 2

What is Psychosis?
Dr Frank Holloway FRCPsych

Introduction

As I write this chapter I am sitting in my study literally surrounded by the books and papers that I have accumulated over the past 40 years. These years have been spent as an undergraduate, medical student, trainee doctor and psychiatrist. Behind me are several hundred crime novels, to my left are several hundred travel books, in front of me a mixed bag of books read and not yet read, at my feet boxes of old papers and to my right a wall of textbooks on psychiatry, philosophy, psychology, mental health law, medical history, biology and sociology. On the landing beside my study is, to the despair of my wife, a further pile of files of material I've squirreled away over the years relating to my professional interests that I haven't yet worked out how to fit into my study (or worked up the resolve to throw away). Directly in front of me is my computer, which has on its hard drive hundreds of documents and presentations relating to my work as a psychiatrist with a special interest in psychosis and its consequences. A click or two away from my desktop is the internet and access to bibliographic databases such as Medline and PsychInfo, and a further click (because I have access to the content of these databases) is the published literature on any topic that might interest me.

It's clear from this anecdote that I live in a world of words (and that I like travel books and crime novels). In my profession as a psychiatrist the key tool I use is the discussion between a patient (and their carers) about the nature of the problems the person is experiencing, backed up by material written in case notes and letters in the past and discussion with other members of the multidisciplinary team. I don't have data on how many people with a diagnosis of psychosis I've treated but in 30 years the numbers must run into the thousands. I have read millions of words about what the term psychosis means and approaches to how I, as a psychiatrist, could help someone who is experiencing psychosis. I have also written or dictated tens of millions of words relating to the treatment and care of my patients who I have diagnosed and treated as suffering from a psychotic illness and hundreds of thousands of words about my views on mental health services that have been published in books and journals.

We live in an information age: as I write this a Google search on the term 'psychosis' provided 4,080,000 sites for me to look at. The two most commonly diagnosed psychotic illnesses, schizophrenia and bipolar affective disorder, identified respectively 8,440,000 and 6,300,000 sites. Anyone with access to a computer can find out most of what has been thought, said and done in relation to 'psychosis', although a lot of what has been thought, said and done is wrong, misleading and potentially unhelpful. In the presence of this mountain of information my task, in some 5,000 words, is to impart my (imperfect – because the field is so vast and contested) knowledge about the topic. It's not for me to say whether my personal knowledge and experience maps onto a degree of wisdom. However the distinction between information, which is available to most of us almost instantaneously; knowledge, which we can acquire if we choose at the cost of significant effort; and wisdom is an important one.

The bulk of this book is made up of the accounts of people who have a lived experience of psychosis. I don't share this lived experience though do have some personal knowledge of the very difficult role of the carer of someone being treated for a psychotic illness. This role is all too often a thankless task that is unnecessarily burdened by guilt.

Definitions

Psychosis is a relatively new word, which initially meant any kind of disordered mental state. It has over the past hundred years come to mean (according to my Shorter Oxford English Dictionary),

'a severe mental illness, derangement, or disorder involving a loss of contact with reality, frequently with hallucinations, delusions, or altered thought processes, with or without a known organic origin'.

Organic, in this context, means a discernable physical cause: examples of organic psychoses would include the grandiose beliefs associated with tertiary syphilis and the hallucinatory voices and persecutory beliefs of someone who is in a delirium caused by an acute infection. In psychiatric jargon 'organic' mental illnesses are contrasted with 'functional' mental illnesses, for which no clear-cut physical cause has been demonstrated. This chapter is focused on the so-called 'functional' psychoses, particularly schizophrenia and bipolar affective disorder. 'Psychosis' is, according to its dictionary definition, inextricably linked with something negative, other from everyday life and experience and perhaps inexplicable. The word 'psychotic' can either be an adjective (for example a psychotic symptom) or a noun (a person with psychosis). When we read about someone being 'psychotic' there is almost invariably a negative tone to the word, which is incidentally often misapplied in the press to someone who has done something bizarre, distasteful or antisocial. Contrast this with 'neurosis',

'a mild mental illness, not attributable to organic disease, characterized by symptoms of stress… without loss of contact with reality'.

Neurosis, in these terms, is something that's more benign and understandable (even, in certain situations rather fashionable) than psychosis and potentially far less stigmatized in popular discourse. In fact all mental disorder attracts stigma and discrimination to a greater or lesser degree.

I have some difficulties with my dictionary about the definitions of neurosis and psychosis. One lies in the 'organic'/'functional' distinction, which goes back to a very old dualism between 'mind' and 'body': our (functional) minds are intimately linked with our (organic) bodies. If you doubt this check your heart rate go up as you watch a frightening film or feel the buzz as you complete a strenuous physical activity. Most psychiatrists, though by no means all, believe that a physical cause (or more likely many causes) will be identified that underlies the so-called 'functional' psychoses: the cause(s) will be interacting with environmental factors to result in the development of a psychotic illness. A second difficulty lies in the view that 'neurotic' disorders cannot by definition have an 'organic' cause – an overactive thyroid can precipitate an anxiety disorder, certain kinds of cancer induce depression (before the diagnosis!) and obsessive-compulsive disorder is a common manifestation of certain specific learning disabilities. It is highly likely that 'neurotic' disorders are associated with significant underlying biological vulnerabilities. A third difficulty is the unrelenting negativity that my dictionary brings to the word 'psychosis' compared with other forms of mental disorder.

Psychotic symptoms and psychotic illnesses

When a psychiatrist or other mental health professional uses the words 'psychosis' and 'psychotic' no negative connotation is intended. The words are being used descriptively, not as value judgements. Psychosis is a term used to cover a range of mental illnesses where psychotic symptoms typically occur. We will come on to what constitutes a 'psychotic symptom' in a moment. Before doing this and to add a bit of necessary confusion, someone can receive a diagnosis of one of the commonest 'psychoses' – bipolar affective disorder (which used to be called 'manic depression') – without ever displaying any psychotic symptoms; people can and do experience psychotic symptoms (particularly hearing voices) without attracting any diagnostic label; and short-term psychotic symptoms (again hearing voices and sometimes feelings of persecution) are a common feature of some mental disorders that are not currently conceptualized as psychoses, particularly some severe forms of personality disorder.

On my bookshelves are four (three of them somewhat elderly) books devoted to a rather unusual topic that few, if any, readers of this book will have heard of – descriptive psychopathology. Many of the psychiatric textbooks I've accumulated have a chapter or more on the topic. Three of the box files on my landing contain structured instruments that can be used by someone with appropriate training to elicit and record psychopathology, which the most recent of my textbooks has neatly termed *Symptoms in the Mind* (Sims, 2003).

The commonest psychotic symptoms are delusions and hallucinations. A delusion is classically defined as:
> *'a false, unshakeable idea or belief which is out of keeping with the patient's educational, cultural and social background; it is held with extraordinary conviction and subjective certainty'* (Sims, 2003 p. 117).

A hallucination is defined as *'a perception without an object'* (Sims, 2003 p. 98). Hallucinations can be in any sensory modality (hearing, sight, smell, taste and bodily sensation). Delusions can either be primary – ie free-standing – or secondary as an explanation for other phenomena, notably hallucinations, or arising from a disturbance in mood. One important, though uncommon, form of primary delusion is *'delusional perception'* where a normal percept (for example, for one of my patients, a man getting up to leave the commuter train he was travelling on) is linked with a delusional belief (the sudden certainty that behind the station where the train had stopped an alien spaceship had landed with the specific aim of making contact with the patient). Another linked set of psychotic phenomena are changes in the way that thoughts are experienced – where thoughts are felt to be withdrawn from the mind, or inserted into the mind from outside or are broadcast for all the world to hear (which can be intensely embarrassing) (Sims 2003, p. 164). People with psychosis, particularly schizophrenia, may also experience a range of *'passivity phenomena'* where the person feels that their emotions, actions or bodily sensations are being imposed on them by an outside agency. A rare, and potentially life-threatening, presentation of psychosis is catatonia where muscle tone is increased: it is associated with gross excitement, odd posturing and stupor – where the person is conscious but unresponsive.

When we think of psychotic symptoms we tend to think in terms of delusions and hallucinations – these are termed '*positive*' symptoms. Equally important in terms of disability and distress are '*negative*' symptoms such as apathy, poverty of speech, social withdrawal and blunting of affect: these can be mimicked by the side-effects of medication and low mood. Yet a further set of symptoms of psychosis lie in the subtle domain of '*formal thought disorder*' which covers a range of phenomena including flight of ideas, where there is an acceleration of the speed of thought and speech, its opposite, retardation, circumstantial thinking (where there are a lot of words but lots of extraneous content), derailment of thinking and thought blocking, where the train of thought quite literally comes to a halt. Finally psychosis, particularly schizophrenia, can be associated with significant impairments in cognitive functioning particularly in memory and what is termed executive functioning, the ability to plan and monitor action.

Making a diagnosis

All doctors, in coming to an understanding of a medical problem, work through a process of taking a history, undertaking an examination and, if necessary, arranging tests. From this will flow a diagnosis and (after negotiation with the patient) a plan for treatment, further monitoring of the presenting problem or agreement that there should be no treatment and any necessary follow-up. Many illnesses are long-term or prone to recurrence so continuing follow-up is often required.

In psychiatry there are no definitive tests to identify an illness in the sense that a blood test can confirm diabetes or an underactive thyroid, an X-ray, CT or MRI the presence of lung cancer and an EEG can confirm a diagnosis of epilepsy. So, at the moment at least, psychiatrists and other mental health professionals depend on the story that the patient and their carers provide and an examination of the person's mental state: from these a diagnosis can be made. Physical tests are usually carried out only to exclude specific physical illnesses if the history suggests that these may be a factor in the presentation or as part of monitoring the person's physical health before treatment is started (treatments can impact on physical health if appropriate precautions are not taken). Because of lack of resources and lack of interest in the issue by psychologists, specific psychological tests that might document the person's current and pre-illness intellectual functioning are very rarely carried out.

By their nature diagnoses place people into categories. It can be argued, with some justification, that many of the phenomena psychiatrists deal with are better seen as lying on a continuum rather than being seen as categorical: When is a somewhat odd idea a delusion? What's the difference between hearing a tune play over in one's mind and a hallucination? Where does muddled thinking stop and formal thought disorder begin? Many people object to the apparently arbitrary nature of psychiatric diagnosis but actually that arbitrariness is intrinsic to a lot of medical practice. Definitions of diabetes or hypertension are arbitrary and even in an apparently high-tech subject like cancer the distinction between an accumulation of malignant cells in the prostate, very common in men of a certain age, and a prostate cancer that requires treatment is by no means clear.

Diagnosing schizophrenia

An example of the story that might be available to the psychiatrist when first meeting a patient is shown in Figure 1.1, which describes a fictional, but not atypical, person called Frank referred to mental health services for the first time. I use this story in training psychiatrists in the use of the Mental Health Act, which allows for compulsory detention and treatment in hospital. Frank's history is highly suggestive of the onset of a psychotic illness and matches some of the vivid first-person accounts in this book. Frank has shown a decline in social functioning of at least six months duration (and in this story probably a lot longer). He has not managed the transition from home to college well and once home has, according to his parents, begun to display odd behaviours, in this story sleep reversal, appearing to talk to himself and covering his bedroom window with aluminium foil, and expressing odd ideas, in this story the concern that the television is talking to him.

Figure 1.1 Frank aged 19

- Previously reasonably successful academically, (though not getting expected grades at A level) he dropped out of college six months ago.

- His GP refers to the psychiatrist following concern from the parents who report he's been talking to himself in his room and complained that the television was referring to him.

- He stays in his room throughout the day – emerging to raid the fridge.

- He has covered the windows of his bedroom with aluminium foil.

The next step would be for the psychiatrist to ask Frank to come and see him/her to check out if the story is true and hear from Frank what's going on from his perspective. If Frank won't come to the clinic the psychiatrist or another member of the team will go and see him. Frank may be reluctant to say what's going on but may tell the psychiatrist that he has been worried that he is the victim of some sort of conspiracy for over a year, he has been hearing voices coming from the street discussing his activities for many months and has tried to talk back to them. He believes that the voices are from the Central Intelligence Agency (CIA) which has a specific interest in him and are projected by some form of electrical energy that should, according to his knowledge of physics, be blocked off by aluminium foil, although this hasn't worked. He finds the voices worse when he is in social situations and they have been much worse when he has tried to leave the house. He is feeling very frightened, very low and has been thinking of suicide. He has also found his thinking very muddled and his studies increasingly difficult in the 18 months before coming into contact with mental health services.

Frank has clear-cut symptoms of psychosis and meets diagnostic criteria for schizophrenia according to International Classification of Disease (ICD-10) and Diagnostic and Statistical Manual (DSM-IV) (which at the time of writing provide the internationally agreed standards for diagnosis). DSM is the diagnostic bible for American psychiatrists (American Psychiatric Association, 2000). ICD is its equivalent for the rest of the world (World Health Organisation, 2003). Both are soon to be replaced by an update – DSM-V in 2013 and ICD-11 in 2015. There are subtle differences between the two systems: mental health professionals in the UK use ICD criteria in clinical practice though often research studies use the slightly more restrictive DSM criteria. Figure 1.2 summarises the ICD-10 criteria for schizophrenia.

Figure 1.2 ICD-10 Diagnostic criteria for schizophrenia

Characteristic symptoms

At least one of:
- thought echo, thought insertion/withdrawal/broadcast
- passivity phenomena
- delusional perception
- third person auditory hallucinations providing a running commentary or discussing the person
- persistent bizarre delusions.

Or two or more of:
- persistent hallucinations in any modality

- thought disorder
- catatonic behaviour (eg excitement, posturing, stupor)
- negative symptoms (eg apathy, poverty of speech, social withdrawal, blunting of affect)
- significant behaviour change.

Duration:
- more than one month.

Exclusion criteria:

- mood disorders, schizoaffective disorder, overt brain disease
- drug intoxication or withdrawal.

Adapted from WHO (1993)

Although everyone who receives a diagnosis of schizophrenia is an individual, but Frank's story is quite typical. About 1% of the population will receive a diagnosis of schizophrenia in their lifetime and the peak age of onset for men is in the late teens and early 20s (it's about four years later for women).

Bipolar affective disorder

Bipolar affective disorder (which used to be known as manic depression) is the other common psychotic illness. It also affects about 1% of the population and again has a peak age of onset in the late teens and early 20s – though can go unrecognized for many years. Unlike depression bipolar disorder is equally common in men and women. It is essentially a disorder of mood with episodes of pathologically low mood and one or more episodes of pathologically elevated mood (mania or hypomania). Mixed states are also common when the irritability, pressured speech and restlessness of hypomania are combined with dysphoria. Again ICD-10 and DSM-IV criteria are similar but subtly different (SIGN, 2005). Although the core feature of bipolar disorder is elevated mood (see Figure 1.3) much of the disability and distress associated with bipolar disorder is found in the depressive symptoms people experience. Between episodes of severe illness people can be completely well – although it is now recognized that chronically low mood is common and may require treatment.

Figure 1.3 Typical features of hypomania and mania

- increased energy, activity, and restlessness
- excessively high, overly good, euphoric mood

- extreme irritability
- racing thoughts and talking very fast, jumping from one idea to another
- distractibility, cannot concentrate well
- little sleep needed
- unrealistic beliefs in one's abilities and powers
- poor judgment
- spending sprees
- a lasting period of behaviour that is different from usual
- increased sexual drive
- abuse of drugs, particularly cocaine, alcohol, and sleeping medications
- provocative, intrusive, or aggressive behaviour
- denial that anything is wrong.

From SIGN Guide 82 Bipolar Affective Disorder

The distinction between hypomania and mania is essentially one of degree: in mania social functioning is grossly disrupted. Both manic and depressive episodes of bipolar disorder can be associated with psychotic symptoms: both delusions – typically in line with the prevailing mood state eg. grandiose and religiose delusions in mania and delusions of worthlessness in depression – and hallucinations (positive or negative voices depending on the prevailing mood state). Persecutory delusions are also common. Manic stupor is a rare and life-threatening presentation of bipolar disorder – it is characterized by non-responsiveness, failure to eat and drink and markedly increased muscle tone.

Other psychoses

Psychotic symptoms (hallucinations saying negative things about one and delusions of worthlessness, guilt or poverty) are quite common in severe depression. Some people exhibit symptoms typical of both schizophrenia and bipolar disorder and receive a diagnosis of 'schizoaffective disorder': this diagnosis is significant because treatments aimed at the schizophrenia (antipsychotic medications) and the mood disorder (mood stabilizers) may both be required. Some people have very brief psychotic episodes that may closely resemble schizophrenia but resolve very rapidly: these 'acute and transient psychotic disorders' (WHO, 1993) may be one-off events or may be a precursor to a later full-blown episode of schizophrenia. Yet another form of psychosis is the 'persistent delusional disorder': this typically starts later in life and is associated with continuing good social functioning but very fixed delusions, with or without hallucinations.

One major issue in diagnosis is when a psychotic episode is associated with substance abuse, particularly cannabis and stimulant drugs such as amphetamines and cocaine. Amphetamines, if taken for long enough and in sufficient quantities, will induce in almost anyone a mental state indistinguishable from schizophrenia and many individuals will begin to experience mild psychotic symptoms when exposed to tetrahydrocannabinol (the most active ingredient in cannabis and skunk). Although there are fears that people who are experiencing the acute effects of drugs are inappropriately labelled as suffering from schizophrenia the opposite problem is likely to be more common – people experiencing an episode of schizophrenia that has been precipitated by consumption of drugs and not getting treatment and follow-up because the problem is labeled a 'drug-induced psychosis'. There are ways of teasing out whether someone is experiencing a primary rather than a substance-induced psychosis (Castle and Buckley, 2008) (See Figure 1.4).

Figure 1.4 Factors suggesting a primary rather than substance-induced psychosis

- Psychotic symptoms came on before the substance misuse.

- Withdrawal of the substance of abuse does not halt the psychotic symptoms (for cannabis up to a month is required to "wash out" the substance).

- Psychotic symptoms continue during times of prolonged abstinence.

- The types of psychotic symptoms are not those usually seen in association with the particular substance used.

- There is a family history of primary psychotic illness.

  (Adapted from Castle and Buckley, 2008)

Co-morbidities

It is extremely common for mental disorders of all kinds to co-occur (Castle and Buckley, 2008). Substance misuse disorder has been reported to occur in 40-60% of people with schizophrenia (although active use is less common) and is also very common indeed in bipolar disorder. It can be very destructive for people living with psychosis in terms of worsening mental health outcomes (particularly hospitalization and once in hospital extended lengths of stay, making violence and victimization more likely, affecting physical health and leading to worsening problems in finances, occupation and housing).

Depressive symptoms are very common amongst people with schizophrenia, both in acute episodes and after the psychosis has abated: all too often these symptoms are put down to negative symptoms of schizophrenia. Up to a quarter of people with schizophrenia meet the criteria for severe depression in their lifetimes and depression plays a part in the risk of suicide amongst people living with schizophrenia (up to one in 20 of people with the diagnosis). Anxiety disorders are also common, particularly social anxiety disorder and obsessive-compulsive disorder. Post-traumatic stress disorder is also being increasingly recognized as a clinical problem: traumas may predate the illness (eg. childhood sexual abuse), may be consequent on the disadvantaged lives that people with psychosis lead (eg. victimization) or be a direct result of the treatment process (eg. seclusion and restraint episodes). Because the focus of interest in treating people with psychosis is usually on the positive symptoms of the illness these important co-morbidities often get missed and consequently don't receive effective treatment.

There is another important aspect to co-morbidity – the increased burden of physical health problems associated with mental illness, particularly schizophrenia. Areas of particular concern are the well-rehearsed consequences of smoking, which is more common amongst people with psychosis, and other increased cardiovascular risk factors: high cholesterol, hypertension, obesity, physical underactivity and diabetes.

Causes

When we go to the doctor about a problem we are generally interested in a number of issues:

- *What's wrong* – a name for the problem?
- *Why did it happen to me* – the reason for the problem?
- *What can be done about it* – the treatments for the problem?
- *What's going to happen to me* – expected outcomes?

It has been one hundred years since the term schizophrenia was coined. Emile Kraepelin made the distinction between affective psychosis and what he termed 'dementia praecox' in 1893, a precursor to what we now call schizophrenia. During this period an enormous amount of research has been undertaken to try and determine the best way of defining psychoses, the causes of psychosis, the outcomes that can be expected and treatments that might improve these outcomes. The past century has seen enormous strides in our understanding of the natural world in terms of the mathematics, physics, chemistry and biology underlying it. There have been exciting advances in genetics, neuro-imaging, pharmacology and psychology. These have helped to throw light on the workings of one of the most complex phenomenon in the universe, the human brain.

Diagnostic manuals such as ICD-10 and DSM-IV now allow us, with reasonable precision, to provide a name for the problems of people experiencing a psychosis. Despite these advances we have to acknowledge that the precise cause(s) of schizophrenia and other psychoses are unknown. Indeed it's quite likely that as our understanding of psychosis improves what we call schizophrenia and bipolar disorder will be redefined as a number of underlying disorders that manifest themselves in rather similar ways.

There are some facts that we do know about the cause(s) of psychosis (Castle and Buckley, 2008). The epidemiology (occurrence in the population) of schizophrenia shows that all populations across the world are at quite similar risk of developing the disorder (roughly 1% of us over a lifetime). There is undoubtedly a genetic effect: we are much more likely to develop schizophrenia if a parent or sibling has the disorder (the risk is in the region of 10%). Identical twins (who share their genes) are more likely to develop schizophrenia than non-identical twins if they have an affected co-twin. These genetic relationships hold if children are adopted away. However this genetic effect is limited. Even where twins are identical there is only a 50% chance of developing schizophrenia if there is an affected co-twin and most people who develop schizophrenia don't have a family history. Despite occasional claims that a 'schizophrenia gene' has been identified it seems clear that there are many genes, each with rather small effect, that contribute to a genetic risk of developing the illness. These genes are likely to be involved in brain development and the way the brain's messaging system (a very complex system involving chemicals called neurotransmitters) works.

Epidemiology has also identified a range of environmental factors that seem to contribute to the risk of developing schizophrenia (Figure 1.5). One of the most intriguing facts to emerge is that the immigration experience has almost uniformly been linked to an increase in the risk of developing schizophrenia. This is unequivocally not a genetic effect and probably relates to the very complex biopsychosocial consequences of immigration and living as a minority ethnic group in the host country.

Figure 1.5 Environmental factors associated with the development of schizophrenia

- season of birth (late winter/early spring)
- exposure to Influenza Type A2 during second trimester of pregnancy
- maternal starvation during first trimester of pregnancy
- maternal stress during pregnancy and pregnancy/birth complications
- paternal age
- urban birth/upbringing
- substance abuse
- migration and ethnic minority status.

(Adapted from Castle and Buckley, 2008)

Since the beginnings of scientific psychiatry attempts have been made to identify abnormalities in the structure or function of the brain that relate to particular mental disorders. There were early initial successes – a notable example is the identification by Alois Alzheimer in 1906 of very specific pathological changes in the brain in people suffering from dementia. No specific changes have ever been identified in people suffering from schizophrenia. Although there is a tendency for people with a diagnosis of schizophrenia to differ on a range of parameters from the general population there is always a substantial degree of overlap. Recent technological advances, particularly in functional brain imaging, throw a fascinating light onto how our brains work both in health and when we are suffering from a mental illness.

One further window onto the causes of schizophrenia might be the treatments we know to be effective against its core symptoms. Antipsychotic medications are undoubtedly effective in alleviating the 'positive' symptoms of schizophrenia, though less so 'negative' symptoms and cognitive deficits (indeed over-treatment can make these worse). These medications work by affecting neurotransmitter systems in the brain, particularly but not exclusively the dopaminergic system. All effective antipsychotics block one particular form of dopamine receptor whilst drugs such as amphetamines and cocaine, which produce psychotic symptoms, stimulate these receptors. The story is complex but this finding has led to the 'dopamine theory' becoming a leading hypothesis about the cause of schizophrenia (Laruelle, 2003). In this theory positive psychotic symptoms are caused by excessive dopaminergic activity in particular parts of the brain, although other neurotransmitter systems have also been implicated (Castle and Buckley, 2008). However the fact that psychological treatments, notably family therapy and cognitive behaviour therapy, can be effective in decreasing symptoms and reducing the risk of relapse, confirms the relevance of social and psychological factors to the onset, remission and relapse of schizophrenia.

Course

We have as yet no clear story about the causes of psychosis (Frith and Johnstone, 2003). The course of psychosis has been studied extensively over the years. It is worth pausing for a moment to consider what the potential impact of experiencing a psychotic illness might be over and above experiencing distressing symptoms. Figure 1.6 describes some of the (negative) impacts on people's life chances of living with a psychosis. There is no doubt that experiencing a mental illness results in significant social exclusion – and one of the key tasks of mental health services is to facilitate social inclusion (Boardman et al, 2010).

Figure 1.6 The impact of psychosis on people's life chances:

- **Low income** – likely to be dependent on benefits.
- **Impoverished, non-reciprocal social networks** – few social contacts and a tendency to be dependent on carers.
- **Poor housing and increased likelihood of becoming homeless.**
- **Unlikely to be employed.**
- **More likely to commit a crime.**
- **More likely to be a victim of crime.**
- **More likely to die young** – because of suicide and physical ill health.
- **Less likely to become a parent.**
- **More likely to raise concerns over parenting skills.**

We have learnt that people with a diagnosis of bipolar disorder do rather worse than we previously believed, at least if continuing depressive symptomatology is not effectively addressed. We have also learnt that people who receive a diagnosis of schizophrenia do a lot better than Kraepelin's original dichotomy between affective psychosis and what he called dementia praecox predicted. A significant proportion of people receiving an initial diagnosis of schizophrenia do very well indeed: one study found that after 15 years 25% were free of symptoms and not on any treatment whilst a further 15% were symptom free and on treatment (Hafner and an der Heiden, 2003). Gone are the days when a diagnosis of schizophrenia meant the possibility of a life-time of hospital care. Clinical recovery or significant improvement is the norm in long-term follow-up studies of schizophrenia (Slade, 2009, pg 36). Even when clinical recovery, as defined by professionals, has not occurred personal recovery is a realistic and important goal. Personal recovery is perhaps more important than the clinical perspective (Slade, 2009).

Treatments

It's beyond the scope of this short chapter to discuss in any detail the treatments that we know work for people living with psychosis. In England and Wales people living with schizophrenia or bipolar disorder should have access to the treatments set out in the Clinical Guidelines developed by the National Institute for Health and Clinical Excellence (NICE). NICE has developed guidelines for the treatment of both bipolar disorder and schizophrenia, which are available on-line as a very full summary of the evidence, a version for professionals and a version for users and carers (NICE, 2006; NICE 2009). Although the focus of these guidelines is on medication, since it is here that the evidence is strongest, the guidelines emphasise the importance of psychological treatments and various kinds of social supports in improving outcomes.

All treatments require a balance between the positive effects of treatment (in the case of antipsychotic medication a high probability that positive psychotic symptoms will improve) and negative effects (which differ between medications and for the particular medication between people). At the heart of both Guidelines is a commitment to a collaborative approach between the mental health professional, the patient and their carers, which is fully compatible with the principles of *Recovery*. However there are circumstances when compulsory treatment may be imposed under the Mental Health Act in the interest of the person's health, their safety or the safety of others – such treatment is always subject to external review and legal appeal.

Conclusion

In this chapter I have tried to describe the ways that psychiatrists come to a diagnosis of psychosis, by obtaining a story of a person's life and identifying key symptoms that fall into a more or less characteristic pattern. I've emphasized the importance of co-morbidity.

I've said something about what we know of the causes of psychosis (an incomplete understanding as yet) and its course (highly variable and much better than people once thought). I've signposted readers to the authoritative guidelines on treatment developed by NICE – which are readily available to the public.

Not everyone gets well in the conventional sense despite the use of NICE-approved treatments and it is in these circumstances that rehabilitation services often become involved: these services can often offer hope to the patient, their carers and the wider service system when hope has been lost (Wolfson et al, 2009).

As yet the Recovery approach, which lies at the heart of this book, has not been subject to the sorts of empirical evaluation that medication and psychological treatments require before becoming generally available, and some would argue that such evaluation is neither necessary nor desirable (Slade, 2009). I disagree.

References

American Psychiatric Association (2000) *Diagnostic and Statistical Manual of Mental Disorders, 4th Edition Revised*. American Psychiatric Association, Washington DC

Boardman J, Currie A, Killaspy H and Mezey G (2010) *Social Inclusion and Mental Health*. RCPsych Publications, London

Castle DJ and Buckley PF (2008) *Schizophrenia*. Oxford University Press, Oxford

Frith C and Johnstone E (2003) *Schizophrenia. A Very Short Introduction*. Oxford University Press, Oxford

Hafner H and an der Heiden W (2003) Course and outcome of schizophrenia. In SR Hirsch and D Weinberger (eds) *Schizophrenia 2nd Edition*. Blackwell, Oxford pp 101-141

Laruelle M (2003) Dopaminergic transmission in the schizophrenic brain. In SR Hirsch and D Weinberger (eds) *Schizophrenia 2nd Edition*. Blackwell, Oxford pp 365-387

NICE (2006) *CG 38 Bipolar disorder. Understanding NICE Guidance*. National Institute for Health and Clinical Excellence, London http://www.nice.org.uk/nicemedia/live/10990/30195/30195.pdf (accessed 26th July 2010)

NICE (2009) *Schizophrenia. Information about Clinical Guideline 82*. National Institute for Health and Clinical Excellence, London

http://www.nice.org.uk/nicemedia/live/11786/43611/43611.pdf
(accessed 26th July 2010)

Scottish Intercollegiate Guidelines Network (2005) Bipolar Affective Disorder. SIGN Guide 82 www.sign.ac.uk (accessed 24th July 2010)

Sims ACP (2003) *Symptoms in the Mind. An Introduction to Descriptive Psychopathology 3rd Edition*. Saunders, London

Slade M (2009) *Personal Recovery and Mental Illness*. Cambridge University Press, Cambridge

Wolfson P, Holloway F and Killaspy H (eds) *Enabling recovery for people with complex mental health needs. A template for rehabilitation services*. Faculty Report FR/RS/1 Faculty of Rehabilitation and Social Psychiatry of the Royal College of Psychiatrists http://www.rcpsych.ac.uk/pdf/fr_rs_1_forwebsite.pdf (accessed 26/7/10)

World Health Organisation (1993) *The ICD 10 classification of mental and behavioural disorders: diagnostic criteria for research*. World Health Organisation, Geneva

Resources

Mental Health Care (http://www.mentalhealthcare.org.uk) provides comprehensive information for service users and carers on all aspects of psychosis and its treatment. It is comprehensive and easy to navigate.

The NICE Guidelines on schizophrenia and bipolar disorder are available on the internet and in hard copy (schizophrenia guideline at http://www.nice.org.uk/nicemedia/live/11786/43611/43611.pdf ;bipolar guideline at http://www.nice.org.uk/nicemedia/live/10990/30195/30195.pdf).

The Royal College of Psychiatrists publishes leaflets on a wide range of mental health problems that include up-to-date information on illnesses and treatments
http://www.rcpsych.ac.uk/mentalhealthinfoforall.aspx

Chapter 3

Recovery: The Long and Winding Road That Leads?
Dr Jerome Carson

Introduction

In 1996, I sat at the front of a large lecture theatre in Rotterdam, Holland, listening to an American clinical psychologist, Patricia Deegan. She gave an inspiring keynote presentation entitled *Recovery As a Journey of the Heart*. I was really only there to hear the second speaker that day, psychiatrist John Strauss, yet it was Patricia Deegan, who was to have the greater influence on my later work. A decade later I moved from the Norwood Community Team to join the South West Sector Community Mental Health Team. The case management teams in Lambeth had been changed into recovery and support teams. I wondered who was it that put the 'recovery' into recovery and support? Initially, I was quite sceptical of the whole recovery approach. The psychiatrist David Whitwell had talked about recovery being a mirage and the myth of recovery. He suggested that survival might be a better term (Whitwell, 1999). Slowly, my own views began to change towards a more pro-recovery stance. In this chapter I outline who and what some of the key influences were in persuading me that recovery was something that I could sign up to. I am going to look at the work of Bill Anthony from America, Retta Andresen and her colleagues from Australia, Julie Leibrich from New Zealand and the work of the influential Sainsbury Centre in the United Kingdom. I then illustrate examples of recovery in practice at both an individual and group level. Let me start though by going back to Patricia Deegan.

Patricia Deegan's *Recovery As a Journey of the Heart*

Patricia Deegan is an American clinical psychologist, who by the age of 18, had been in mental hospital three times. Her subsequent journey of recovery and reflections on the process, are described in two key papers (Deegan, 1988; Deegan, 1996). The second paper on *Recovery as a Journey of the Heart* was the one she presented in Rotterdam. I purchased the video of this presentation and have used it in teaching sessions with both staff and service users and in the process have watched it over a hundred times. It is probably the single most influential paper I have ever read on recovery. Deegan reminds us that the goal of recovery, "...is to become the unique, awesome, never to be repeated human being, that we are called to be," (Deegan, 1996, p.92). Yet for several years in the early period of her illness, she made little progress. She recounts that when aged 18 she asked the psychiatrist what was wrong with her, he replied, "You have a disease called chronic schizophrenia. It is a disease like diabetes. If you take your medications for the rest of your life and avoid stress, then maybe you can cope," (p. 92). She described this as getting a "prognosis of doom."

One of Deegan's main contributions was to show how Martin Seligman's theory of learned helplessness might explain the supposedly unmotivated behaviour of many individuals with long term mental health problems (Seligman, 1975). Like many of these people, Deegan gave up, but as she explains, "...giving up was not a problem it was a solution, because it protected me from wanting anything. If I didn't want anything it couldn't be taken away. If I didn't try, then I wouldn't have to undergo another failure. If I didn't care then nothing could hurt me again. My heart became hardened.... becoming hard of heart and not caring anymore is a strategy that people who are at the brink of losing hope adopt in order to remain alive," (p. 93). She argues, it is "safer to become helpless than to become hopeless," (p. 94).

She suggested that professionals needed to do three things to work with service users in this state of helplessness. First, she said we should try and see "the behaviour in terms of its existential significance," (p. 95). What is it we might be expecting individuals to risk when we ask them to embark on a particular course of action? Second, she states we should try and see service users as heroes. Could we have survived many of the things they have had to deal with in life? Would we be able to manage on benefits and cope with the effects of a major mental disorder at the same time? Third, she says that while professionals may not be able to change the person they are working with, they can change the human interactive environment. We need to "role model hope and continue to offer options and choices even if they are rejected over and over again," (p. 95) (see Figure 2.1).

Figure 2.1 Deegan's three steps to help service users overcome helplessness

1. See the behaviour in terms of its existential significance
2. See service users as heroes
3. Try to change the human interactive environment by offering hope.

Deegan defines recovery thus:

'Recovery does not mean cure. Rather recovery is an attitude, a stance, and a way of approaching the days challenges...There are times of rapid gains and disappointing relapses. There are times of just living, just staying quiet, resting and regrouping. Each person's journey of recovery is unique. Each person must find what works for them,' (p. 96-97).

Her perspective on recovery is unique, as it embraces a service user and a professional perspective (see also Emma Harding's chapter in this book).

Bill Anthony's guiding vision of recovery

Bill Anthony, a psychiatry professor from Boston, has for many years been one of the leading authorities in psychiatric rehabilitation. In another classic paper (Anthony, 1993), he described how recovery has emerged largely from service user accounts and not professionals. His definition of recovery is one of the most cited professional definitions,

'Recovery is described as a deeply personal, unique process of changing one's attitudes, values, feelings, goals, skills and/or roles. It is a way of living a satisfying, hopeful and contributing life even with limitations caused by illness. Recovery involves the development of new meaning and purpose in life as one grows beyond the catastrophic effects of mental illness,' (Anthony, 1993, p.15).

He goes on to set out eight assumptions of recovery-focused services (see Figure 2.2).

Figure 2.2 Anthony's eight assumptions of recovery-focused services

> 1 Recovery can happen without professional intervention. It is not professionals who hold the keys to recovery, it is service users.
>
> 2 A common feature of recovery stories is the presence of people who believe in and stand by the person in need of recovery.
>
> 3 The recovery vision does not relate to a specific theory about the aetiology of mental illness. Recovery can occur whether you believe the cause of mental illness to be biological or not.
>
> 4_Recovery can occur even though symptoms can come back.
>
> 5 Recovery changes the frequency and duration of symptoms. When an individual has embarked on their recovery journey, symptoms interfere with functioning less often and for shorter periods of time.
>
> 6 Recovery is not a linear process. It can be the opposite of being systematic and planned.

---

7 Recovery from the consequences of mental illness can be harder than recovery from the illness itself. For instance it may be very hard for someone diagnosed with schizophrenia to obtain employment due to discrimination.

8 Recovery from mental illness does not mean that one was not really mentally ill in the first place. It is not unknown for psychiatrists to say that the original diagnosis must have been wrong, when a patient with schizophrenia makes a very good recovery.

In terms of the recovery vision Anthony suggests, "A vision begets not false promises but a passion for what we are doing," (p. 22). He argues that previous service visions may not have been focused enough on service users. Recovery from mental illness is, he feels, a very potent vision. "It speaks to the heretofore unmentioned and perhaps heretical belief that any person with severe mental illness can grow beyond the limits imposed by his/her illness," (p. 22). He ends the paper by stating, "Recovery is a concept that can open our eyes to new possibilities for those we serve and how we can go about serving them. The 1990s might also turn out to be the decade of recovery," (p. 22). In fact in Britain, it is the first decade of the twenty-first century that has turned out to be the decade of recovery due to the level of research and publications being produced here. But before looking at British influences on recovery, I turn to examine contributions from pioneers in recovery from Australia and New Zealand.

Components and stages of the recovery process

Research psychologist Retta Andresen and her colleagues Lindsay Oades and Peter Caputi studied the published literature on service user recovery (Andresen at al, 2003). From looking at these reports, they came up with a psychological definition of recovery as,

> 'The establishment of a fulfilling, meaningful life and a positive sense of identity founded on hopefulness and self-determination,' (p. 588).

They identified four key components of recovery (see Figure 2.3).

Figure 2.3 Andresen's four components of recovery

---

1 **Hope**. They found references to hope in 19 out of 28 consumer accounts, in nine out of ten consumer articles and in all eight qualitative studies. "Hope was described as coming from within the person, or as being triggered by a significant other, peer or a role model," (p. 589).

2 **Self-identity.** A severe mental illness can erode an individual's sense

---

of identity. The key according to one author is to know yourself, know your illness and to know the difference between the two. Another writer commented that if the illness and the person become one, then there is no one left inside to take on the work of recovery.

3 **Meaning in life**. After the development of a major mental disorder, each individual may have to reappraise their meaning and purpose in life, as their "previous life goals may not be available to them," (p. 590). That meaning will vary with each individual.

4 **Personal responsibility**. This involves lifestyle choices, the use of medication, personal accountability and the willingness to take risks. This is also referred to as self-determination. What responsibility am I going to take for my situation?

A second important aspect of the work that Andresen and her colleagues conducted was coming up with a stage model of the recovery process. They identified five distinct stages of the process (p. 591) (see Figure 2.4).

Figure 2.4 Andresen's five stages of the recovery process

Stage 1. **Moratorium**: This is a period which is characterised by "denial, confusion, hopelessness, identity confusion and self-protective withdrawal,"
Stage 2. **Awareness**: Here the person "has a first glimmer of hope of a better life and that recovery is possible."
Stage 3. **Preparation**: In this stage the individual starts the work of recovery. This can involve learning about mental illness and local services, getting involved in groups and linking up with peers.
Stage 4. **Rebuilding**: Here the person works to develop a positive identity. This stage focuses on taking responsibility for managing the illness and taking control of their life.
Stage 5. **Growth**: This is the final stage of recovery. Here the person knows how to self-manage their illness and stay well. They have a 'full and meaningful life" and a "positive sense of self."

In a second paper, Andresen et al (2006), describe the development of the Stage of Recovery Instrument (STORI). This is a tool to assess which stage of recovery an individual service user is at. The STORI consists of 50 items each rated from zero to five, presented in groups of five, with one item in each group representing a different stage of recovery. They also developed the Self-Identified Stage of Recovery Scale (SISR), a single-item scale of five statements, each corresponding to their five stage model of recovery. I have found this to be quite helpful in my work with service users.

The work of Retta Andresen and her colleagues has been especially helpful for my understanding of recovery for two main reasons. First, they have helped identify four key components of recovery although there are of course others (see Onken et al, 2007). Second, they have developed a five stage model of the recovery process and have provided us with two measures, STORI and SISR, to be able to map this with service users. Their stage model has also influenced others and the development of the Mental Health Recovery Star, follows a similar framework (McKeith and Burns, 2008, a, b).

The gift of *A Gift of Stories*

In an e-interview for the *Psychiatric Bulletin* (2008), consultant psychiatrist in rehabilitation and recovery Glenn Roberts described *A Gift of Stories* as the best book ever written on recovery. The book contains 21 stories featuring individuals with the complete range of mental health problems, from diverse backgrounds. While there are other similar books (Barker et al, 1999; Chandler and Hayward, 2009), none is as lavishly illustrated, or as well produced as this set of fascinating stories gathered by psychologist Julie Leibrich (Leibrich, 1999).

In the postscript to her own chapter Leibrich describes the process thus, "I started simply by thinking about recovery....However as I listened to people, I began to struggle with the word recovery. Some people in the book were quite comfortable with the word recovery and talked about stages of recovery....As people talked about dealing with illness, their stories were about the progressive discovery of solutions....People talked about the discoveries they had made about themselves...So at this point in my understanding if there is one word I would choose to describe what I heard throughout this work, it would be discovery...Right now the best way I can describe dealing with mental illness is making our way along an ever-widening spiral of discovery in which we uncover problems, discover the best ways to deal with them, recover ground that has been lost, discover new things about ourselves, then uncover deeper problems, discover the best ways....and so on in an intricate process of growth," (p. 180-181). This is an amazing and inspiring book and if I could recommend only one book to read about recovery, this would be it.

Policy drivers towards making recovery a reality

There have been many reports written on recovery in Britain in recent years. The National Institute of Mental Health in England's guiding statement on recovery (NIMHE, 2005) lists 12 principles for recovery based services, with number one stating that the user determines if and when to start the recovery process. In *Whose Recovery is it Anyway?* the Social Perspectives Network published material from a set of workshops and presentations taken from a recovery study day (SPN, 2007). One of the papers expressed a worry that,

"...the recovery agenda is being colonised by mental health services and inevitably being re-articulated," (p. 5). Mental health charity Mind produced the findings from a round table discussion called, *The Life and Times of a Supermodel* (Mind, 2008). This produced a very lively debate with concerns expressed about changes to the welfare system and the narrow focus on employment as the Holy Grail of recovery, among other matters. *New Horizons* set out the future vision for mental health services, broadening the debate to focus on wellbeing as well as recovery (Department of Health, 2009). The most important recovery report was probably the one produced by the Sainsbury Centre for Mental Health entitled, *Making Recovery a Reality,* (Shepherd et al, 2008).

The Sainsbury Centre Report is important as it sets out in detail how to develop recovery-focused mental health services, stating, "Recovery is an idea whose time has come," (p. 1). It starts by pointing out how the recovery approach has been endorsed in countries including Australia and New Zealand, by Department of Health policies, by mental health Trusts across Britain and by the different professions. They also draw attention to the fact that another impetus for the focus on recovery has been the generally positive results from long term outcome studies of people diagnosed with schizophrenia (Davidson and McGlashan, 1996; Dorrer, 2006). One of the central tenets of the Sainsbury Report is that it recommends a different working relationship between service users and professionals (Roberts and Wolfson, 2004). Professionals need to provide service users with the resources in terms of information, skills, networks and supports to help them manage their conditions. They quote the statement from Repper and Perkins (2003), that professionals need to move from a position of "being on-top to being on-tap." It is interesting to speculate how many professionals might be willing to adopt such an approach. Shepherd et al (2008) are also very keen that employment should be a key priority for recovery based services.

The authors of the report articulate what they believe are the key practitioner skills required of professionals. They cite work conducted in Norway by Borg and Kristiansen (2004), which emphasised that professionals need to be open, collaborate as equals, focus on the service user's inner resources, have reciprocal relationships and show a willingness "to go the extra mile." In their paper which comprised a series of in-depth qualitative interviews with service users, one service user commented how her community nurse visited her when she was "off duty." Another described how her psychiatrist brought her with him when he changed jobs three times in six years. Shepherd describes ten points for reflection after sessions with service users (see Figure 2.5).

Figure 2.5 Shepherd's ten reflective questions for mental health professionals

1 Did I listen to help the person make sense of their mental health problems?

2 Did I help the person identify and prioritise their personal goals?

3 Did I show I believed in the person's strengths and resources to achieve their goals?

4 Did I provide examples of other inspiring service users?

5 Did I encourage the person to focus more on their potential contributions to others and away from the "sick role?"

6 Did I identify how friends, non-health service organisations and others might help the person achieve their goals?

7 Did I encourage self-management of their mental health problems?

8 Did I discuss what therapeutic interventions they might want?

9 Did I show respect for the person and try and work in an equal partnership, showing a willingness "to go the extra mile?"

10 Did I provide continuing support maintaining the person's hope and expectations?

This is a very challenging list of demands for staff. The authors of the report also suggest applying similar standards and questions to teams (see Figure 2.6).

Figure 2.6 Shepherd's questions for healthcare teams dealing with service users

1 Are there opportunities for service users to be employed in the team?

2 Does the team encourage user involvement in decisions about treatment and management plans?

3 Is the team leader committed to ensuring that staff show the attitude of respect and equality to the service user?

4 Does the monitoring of the quality of recovery oriented practice appear in individual job descriptions and feature in the personal appraisals of staff? (p. 9) (Shepherd, 2008).

Ultimately, these ideas need to be part of the policy of the wider organisation. Their suggestions for how this might be done include the following:

5 Does the organisation have a recovery mission statement?
6 What focus is there on staff training and who should deliver this?
7 Are service users employed by the organisation? In what proportions?
8 Can existing staff contribute their own lived experience with mental health problems?
9 How is stigma addressed in recruitment and HR procedures?

After publishing this first paper, the Sainsbury Centre team conducted workshops on recovery in five mental health Trusts in 2008/9. They identified ten key organisational challenges for mental health services (Sainsbury Centre, 2009) (see Figure 2.7).

Figure 2.7 Sainsbury Centre ten key organisational challenges for mental health services

1 Changing the nature of the day-to-day interactions and the quality of experience.
2 Delivering comprehensive, service user-led education and training programmes.
3 Establishing a Recovery Education Centre to drive the programmes forward.
4 Ensuring organisational commitment: creating the culture.
5 Increasing personalisation and choice.
6 Changing the way we approach risk assessment and management.
7 Redefining service user involvement.
8 Transforming the workforce.
9 Supporting staff in their recovery journey.
10 Increasing opportunities for building a life beyond illness.

Finally in a third policy paper (Shepherd, Boardman and Burns, 2010), the authors provide a framework for assessing how services are performing on each of the ten organisational challenges, described in their earlier paper (Sainsbury Centre, 2009). Each challenge is rated at one of three levels.

Stage 1 is **engagement.** The organisation is engaged in its attempt to provide recovery-oriented services, but there has been little progress thus far.

Stage 2 is **development**. Some action will have been taken within the organisation. Some services are delivered in a recovery-focused way, but this is not consistent across the Trust.

Stage 3 is **transformation**. Here the vision has been realised. Policies, processes and practices deliver a recovery-oriented service at each level of the organisation from Boards to teams to front line workers.

If we just consider one of the ten challenges, for example, challenge three, 'Establishing a Recovery Education Centre to drive the programmes forward,' at the top level Stage 3, **transformation**, we would see the following, "This would be staffed and run by user trainers and deliver support and training for service users to train staff in recovery principles for teams and for wards.... The Centre also runs programmes to train service users as peer professionals, to work alongside traditional mental health professionals as direct care staff....The Centre offers courses to service users, their families and carers on recovery and the possibilities of self-management. There are a range of links to general educational classes in the community and pathways to courses and other learning opportunities," (p. 10). The authors provide examples of outcome indicators, eg, the establishment of a Recovery Education Centre with stable funding, employing at least three or four service user trainers. They also list a range of possible data sources, eg, the number of peer-led training courses run.

Finally, they provide a template for judging the service on the ten organisational challenges as falling at Stage 1, 2 or 3 with a priority for action (Template A). They also present another template that sets out an action plan to improve the score for the organisational challenge with local goals agreed by commissioners and providers and specific actions to make progress on these goals before the next review.

Local recovery initiatives

The theory of recovery is one thing, but how you put it into practice is another. The work in which a number of us have been engaged, in the Lambeth South West Sector in South London, has largely been conducted on an individual and a group basis. I will provide two examples of each below. In terms of individual work, I am going to talk about the work with two service users, Michelle McNary (see also her chapter in this book) and the *Recovery Film* and Matt Ward and the play *St Nicholas*. In terms of group based approaches, I will talk about the Recovery Group and Recovery Workshops.

Individual recovery work

Michelle McNary had been working with a number of my clinical psychology trainees. As this work had reached something of an impasse, I offered to see her personally. At one of our first sessions, Michelle said that she wanted to write a script about her experiences as an inpatient. She was however, having difficulty getting this written. It seemed to me that maybe she was too close to the story to be able to write fluently at this stage. I suggested instead that as she was a trained film director, she make a film about recovery. We were both enthused by this idea, yet how would we make it happen? From a professional point of view I felt I needed to get some support from a fellow colleague. I approached consultant psychiatrist Frank Holloway, the Medical Director for Croydon Integrated Mental Health Services. Frank not only agreed to join in, but also came up with the idea of inviting Paul Wolfson to become a part of the project team as he was a fellow consultant psychiatrist who had not only written on the topic of recovery (Roberts and Wolfson, 2004), but had previous experience as a scriptwriter. We had a project team, but no money. I then approached Jill Lockett, who was then the Business Manager for the South London and Maudsely NHS Foundation Trust and also met with Dan Charlton, the Trust Head of Communications. Not only were they interested in the idea of a film, they knew exactly what they wanted. This was a 20 minute film that could be downloaded free from the Internet so it could be easily accessible to all. Following this meeting Michelle and I set about drawing up a budget for the film. We met with Jill Lockett to finalise the budget, but it was to be a few more months before we secured the £20,000 to make the film. We were joined later by Godfried Attafua, who managed the budget and Gilly Sykes, whom Michelle chose to be her production manager. Michelle and Paul Wolfson conducted auditions for service users and eventually four were chosen to appear in the film.

While Michelle was busy making the film, I set myself the additional and more personally comfortable task of co-editing the book of the film, *Recovery Journeys* (Carson et al, 2008). This comprised three papers from the professionals in the team, one from Michelle on making the film and four individual accounts from the stars of the film, the service users. As Michelle had also set herself the task of editing the film, it did not come out until April 2010. After some initial technical difficulties, the film was put onto YouTube and also the Trust website.

My recovery role was to try and obtain the resources to enable Michelle to make the film and to support her during the process. At times this involved mediating between Michelle and the Charitable Trustees or the Communications Department. Our own clinical work shifted towards a focus on the *Recovery Film*. This meant that Michelle's clinical needs were somewhat neglected. We solved this by arranging for Michelle to receive some additional cognitive analytic therapy, which she found very helpful. Personally, I always believed that the *Recovery Film* was the best step that I could help Michelle take on her own individual journey of recovery. None of this would have been possible if Michelle did not have the professional background in film making, including a Masters degree in the subject. My hope is that the film will serve as a stepping stone to other projects, including the original idea that Michelle wanted to work on, her own story, to be called *Climbing Walls*.

Matt Ward, St Nicholas and his *Recovery: A Work in Progress*

I was introduced to the actor Matt Ward by his occupational therapist, Davina Blunt. Matt agreed to read out a selection of service user poetry at a World Mental Health Day event. He subsequently attended a couple of our Recovery Group meetings. Meeting him in the street outside our team base one day, I asked if he could present anything to the group. He said he did a one-man play called *St Nicholas*, written by the Irish playwright Conor McPherson. This was 90 minutes long. I had the feeling that this was going to be something special. I approached Yvonne Farquharson, the Performing Arts manager of the Guy's and St Thomas' Charity and invited her to come and watch the play. The 16 people who were present for that first performance of St Nicholas witnessed something truly special.

Some weeks later, Matt and I went to visit Yvonne at Guy's Hospital. She agreed to award us £2,500. We worked out that this would enable us to put on five performances of the play in Lambeth. Matt's wife Marian, persuaded her employers to produce the poster and flyers for the play free of charge. I booked the five venues. Our first night was at the Stockwell YMCA for an evening performance. Only ten people attended, and two of these were my daughter and her friend, whom I had asked along to help with the refreshments. The next performance was the following day back at the Streatham team base. We had 29 people at this, including 26 staff. Two days later Matt gave a phenomenal performance at Nettlefold Hall in West Norwood Library. This was seen by only 16 people, in a theatre that held 175. Our first week had not been an unqualified success. The second week started with a performance in the dining room at Lambeth Hospital. We again had 29 attendees. The final performance was held at Governor's Hall in St Thomas' Hospital and was attended by 85 people. Matt's performance matched the setting on what was a magical evening.

My recovery roles in Matt's play were multiple. I booked the venues, bought and helped serve the refreshments, was the MC, drove Matt and his father on the last night to all the venues. I helped arrange the seating. I photocopied all the handouts and collated them into folders with the help of my wife and sons. After each play I joined Matt on stage to ask him about his own recovery. Following my interview, the audience were asked to complete a short questionnaire about the play and attitudes towards recovery. Yvonne had wanted the play not only to be entertaining, but also to have an educational component (see Ward et al, 2010).

What was the role of the play in Matt's own recovery from bipolar disorder? In fact Matt had already been thinking about his recovery as he gave a presentation at the Lambeth Recover Me conference entitled *My Recovery: A Work in Progress*. In this he combined his love of Shakespeare, reciting relevant sections from *Macbeth*, *Hamlet* and *King Lear*, interspersed with his personal narrative of his battles with bipolar. It is a presentation that he has now given in several different venues and to professional, lay and service user audiences. His recovery has progressed in leaps and bounds since.

Groupwork in recovery - The Recovery Group

I started the Recovery Group in November 2007 with the aim of promoting the concept of recovery to service users. The first talk and presentation was by a service user who is both a talented artist and photographer. It was attended by over 20 people. A month later we had our second session by Michelle and myself, the only joint one between a service user and a professional. This was entitled, *Recovery: Do service users hold the keys to our understanding?* This was attended by ten people and was the first time Michelle had talked in public about the recovery film that she was going to be working on. One of the most remarkable early sessions was Gordon McManus' interview in February 2008 (see his chapter in this book). While Gordon lectured in business studies before his breakdown, he was reluctant to face a room full of people on his own. We hit on the idea of me interviewing him. We decided to use the model of his recovery that we developed together (McManus et al, 2009), as the focus of the presentation. Gordon felt that it took him at least three days to recover from this first public presentation. Two years later, along with Matt Ward and myself, he gave the same presentation to 45 social work Masters degree students at Kingston University. Audiences have been awed by his intellectual and personal understanding of recovery.

Sarah Morgan and myself wrote an article on the early stages of the Recovery Group (Morgan and Carson, 2009). The idea behind the Recovery Group is that the service users are the stars. They do the presentations, not professionals. Topics chosen are ones where they have a particular talent or story to tell. Marie-Therese Barrett gave two presentations, the first on *Can art uplift you?*, the second on her love for Japanese art. Liz Wakely talked about history and hope. She showed how Winston Churchill, Charles Darwin and Florence Nightingale in some ways benefited from their mental illnesses, in that this led them to become more focussed in their respective fields. Margaret Muir talked about *Lessons from the University of Life*. We have only had two outside speakers thus far. Mark Brown, the editor of *One in Four* magazine, shared the story of why he developed an aspirational lifestyle magazine for people with mental illness. Peter Chadwick (see his chapter in this book) came down in June 2009 to talk about *Positive perspectives on psychosis*. This was our most successful session, attended by 50 people.

My recovery role in the Recovery Groups has been to arrange the speakers, and if necessary, provide them with the coaching or reassurance to help them believe that they can put on an interesting presentation. I send out flyers in advance to people on our mailing list of 50 to 60 service users. I also arrange the refreshments for each group. During the groups, I introduce and thank the speakers, serve the refreshments and tidy up afterwards. Does the group help with peoples' recovery? I would hope that it provides a lot of inspiration for attendees, and that speakers can be role models for other people, who may be not as far along their own personal journeys of recovery. These sessions run every six to eight weeks, but this autumn will move to fortnightly.

Recovery workshops

Within the South London and Maudsley NHS Foundation Trust, several hundred staff benefited from four days training in recovery under the Retrain Project, established by research psychologist Mike Slade and consultant psychiatrist Tom Craig. On Day One trainees were provided with an overview of the recovery field. Days Two and Three were based on the *Psychosis Revisited* pack (Bassett et al, 2007). These were run in workshop format, as was Day Four. This last day comprised the service user perspective, social inclusion, the carer viewpoint and spirituality. However no systematic training has been offered to service users.

To address this training gap, I developed a ten week Recovery Workshop programme. This was funded by the Lambeth Executive and the South London and Maudsley Charitable Trustees. Both workshops cost around £1,800. The content of the programme was as follows:

- Introduction to recovery
- Self-esteem and gratitude
- Spirituality and hope
- Friendship and family
- Wellbeing and lifestyle
- Work and leisure
- Identity and meaning
- Stigma and personal responsibility
- Goals and strengths
- Reflections and personal journeys.

The format of the sessions was roughly similar with the sessions running in two parts over three hours, including lunch and a break. The first set of ten workshops was run by me, assisted by a service user co-facilitator (who received £660 for the ten workshops) and an occupational therapist. The second set of workshops was run by me and another service user co-facilitator. We brought in other service users to teach on specific topics. Matt Ward did a session on identity, Esther Maxwell-Orumbie (see her chapter in this book) ran a session on personal responsibility. We brought in other staff to present on other topics. Sherry Clark ran a session on wellbeing, Julia Head, the Trust Head of Chaplaincy, ran the session on spirituality, Sarah Gladstone did the session on work, and Pauline Etim-Ubah facilitated a session on stigma.

Participants in the workshops received comprehensive handouts and folders, free sandwich lunches and refreshments. At the end of the workshops, participants were invited for a meal at a local restaurant. Here they were presented with their course certificates and copies of the course book *A Gift of Stories*. The first set of workshops had an average of six attendees and the second eight. Uptake was not as high as I had expected. Pre and post evaluations were completed, but the results of these have not yet been analysed. Funding has been secured to run another three sets of workshops. The programme for these will be simplified to cover one topic only per session.

My roles in the Recovery Workshop have again been varied. First, I had to secure funding to run the workshops, which meant drawing up a reasoned application, backed by research. Second, I had to arrange all the sessions, provide the teaching material and handouts and book the speakers. Third, I co-facilitated the workshops with the service user co-facilitator. Both service users attended all ten sessions as required, however on two occasions one was too depressed to contribute, and I was left to lead the workshop on my own. Additionally I purchased the groceries and refreshments for each session, arranged the food and tidied up afterwards.

Reflections on recovery and the role of the professional

Both service user Gordon McManus and psychiatrist Glenn Roberts (Roberts, 2009) have stated that recovery is hard work for the service user. Earlier we examined at length the *Making Recovery a Reality* report from the Sainsbury Centre. This provided a list of ten points for reflection for the professional, trying to work in a recovery oriented way. What these experts fail to mention is that recovery is hard work for the staff as well! The interventions I described above were completed sometimes as part of my job, but often on top of my job. This work has been exceptionally rewarding and fulfilling and probably the most exciting of my professional career, but it has been very hard work.

I have often been struck by two of the comments from the *Making Recovery a Reality* report. The first is the notion of professionals "being on tap not on top." Is this ever truly possible? Do mental health professionals want to be at the "beck and call" of their service users? The second is "going the extra mile." If staff are overworked and burned out, they are unlikely to want to "go the extra mile." Yet, it is the staff who do "go the extra mile" that are undoubtedly most appreciated by service users.

There is also a danger of clinical needs getting neglected, if there is too great a focus on recovery project work. I have certainly found this in my own work. Sessions with service users can end up focusing on the progress of the recovery projects, with not enough attention being devoted to clinical problems. In Michelle's case this was solved by securing additional therapeutic input.

I have tried to develop a partnership model of working, yet is a true partnership ever possible given that one person is providing their services free, while the other is being paid for working with that individual? Without the input of the professional however, it may be much harder for the service user to secure the resources to develop their own recovery plan. Many charities refuse to accept applications from individual service users, but only from professionals on their behalf. Some service users may not have the knowledge of what resources are there to help them, or the ability to complete the application forms. I have always been very careful to ensure that I thank charitable bodies on behalf of awards made to service users, and to keep them updated as to the progress of our recovery work. In my experience this is something that some service users forget.

Conclusions

"Recovery is an idea whose time has come," (Shepherd et al, 2008). In this chapter I have looked at contributions from many professionals working in the field of recovery. Patricia Deegan has a unique perspective, embracing service user and professional perspectives. She suggested the goal of recovery was "to become the unique, awesome, never to be repeated human being that we are called to be." Bill Anthony suggested recovery was a vision for mental health services in the 1990s, yet here we are in Britain near the end of 2010, with the vision still not realised. Retta Andresen and her colleagues specified the four key components of recovery and the five stages in the process. Like this book, Julie Leibrich gathered 21 service user accounts for her book *A Gift of Stories*. I summarised the work from the Sainsbury Centre team and their influential report *Making Recovery a Reality*, along with subsequent work on how to put their ideas into practice. I then gave examples of local recovery initiatives that I have been involved with in Lambeth at both an individual and a group level. So whose recovery is it anyway? It is of course the service user's recovery. This book places the service user centre stage. However service users and professionals need each other to achieve the goal of a more recovery-focused service. Recovery is hard work, but it has the capacity to be truly transformative. Michelle's film will hopefully be recognised as a major contribution to the service user perspective on recovery. Matt's plays were incredibly moving to those of us who witnessed them. I was privileged to have been able to work with both individuals. The road to recovery is a long and winding one, but it leads to a better future for the service user, and a more fulfilling job for the professional.

References

Andresen R, Oades L and Caputi P (2003) The experience of recovery from schizophrenia: Towards an empirically validated stage model. *Australian and New Zealand Journal of Psychiatry,* **37**, 5, 586-594

Andresen R, Caputi P and Oades L (2006) Stages of Recovery Instrument: Development of a measure of recovery from severe mental illness. *Australian and New Zealand Journal of Psychiatry,* **40**, 10, 972-980

Anthony W (1993) Recovery from mental illness: Guiding vision of mental health service systems in 1990s. *Psychosocial Rehabilitation Journal,* **16**, 4, 11-23

Barker P, Campbell P and Davidson B (eds) (1999) *From the Ashes of Experience: Reflections on Madness, Survival and Growth.* Whurr: London

Bassett T, Cooke A and Read J (2003) *Psychosis Revisited: A workshop for mental health workers.* Pavilion: Brighton

Borg M and Kristiansen K (2004) Recovery-oriented professionals: Helping relationships in mental health services. *Journal of Mental Health,* **13**, 493-505

Carson J, Holloway F, Wolfson P and McNary M (eds) (2008) *Recovery Journeys: Stories of coping with mental health problems.* South London and Maudsley NHS Foundation Trust: London

Chandler R and Hayward M (eds) (2009) *Voicing Psychotic Experiences: A reconsideration of recovery and diversity.* Pavilion: Brighton

Davidson, L and McGlashan T (1997) The varied outcomes of schizophrenia. *Canadian Journal of Psychiatry,* **42,** 34-43

Deegan, P www.patdeegan.com
Deegan P (1988) Recovery: The lived experience of rehabilitation. *Psychosocial Rehabilitation Journal,* **11**, 4, 11-19

Deegan P (1996) Recovery as a journey of the heart. *Psychiatric Rehabilitation Journal,* **19**, 3, 91-97

Department of Health (2009) *New Horizons: Towards a Shared Vision for Mental Health.* Department of Health: London

Dorrer N (2006) *Evidence of Recovery: The ups and downs of longitudinal outcome research.* Scottish Recovery Network: Glasgow

Fannon, D (2008) E-interview with Dr Glenn Roberts. *Psychiatric Bulletin,* **32**, 2, p. 80

Leibrich, J (1999) *A Gift of Stories.* University of Otago Press: Dunedin

McKeith J and Burns S (2008, a) *Mental Health Recovery Star: User Guide.* Mental Health Providers Forum: London

McKeith J and Burns S (2008, b) *Mental Health Recovery Star: Organisational Guide.* Mental Health Providers Forum: London

McManus G, Morgan S, Fradgley J and Carson J (2009) Recovery heroes - A profile of Gordon McManus. *A Life in the Day,* **13**, 4, 16-19

Mind (2008) *Life and Times of a Supermodel: The recovery paradigm for mental health.* MindThink Report 3. Mind: London:

Morgan S and Carson, J (2009) The recovery group: A service user and professional perspective. *Groupwork,* **19**, 1, 26-39

National Institute for Mental Health in England (2005) *NIMHE Guiding Statement on Recovery.* Department of Health: London

Onken S, Craig C, Ridgway P, Ralph R and Cook J (2007) An analysis of the definitions and elements of recovery: A review of the literature. *Psychiatric Rehabilitation Journal,* **31**, 1, 9-22

Repper J and Perkins R (2003) *Social Inclusion and Recovery: A model for mental health practice.* Balliere Tindall: London

Roberts G and Wolfson P (2004) The rediscovery of recovery: Open to all. *Advances in Psychiatric Treatment*, **10**, 1, 37-48

Roberts G (2009) Coming home. In, Davidson L. and Lynn L (eds) *Beyond the Storms: Reflections on personal recovery in Devon*. Devon Partnership NHS Trust: Exeter

Sainsbury Centre for Mental Health (2009) *Implementing Recovery: A new framework for organisational change*. Position Paper. Sainsbury Centre for Mental Health: London

Seligman M (1975) *Helplessness: On Depression, Development and Death*. Freeman: San Francisco

Shepherd G, Boardman J and Slade M (2008) *Making Recovery a Reality*. Sainsbury Centre for Mental Health: London

Shepherd G, Boardman G and Burns M (2010) *Implementing Recovery: A methodology for organisational change*. Sainsbury Centre for Mental Health: London

Social Perspectives Network (2007) *Whose Recovery is it Anyway?* Social Perspectives Network: London

Ward M, Chander A, Robinson S, Farquharson Y and Carson J (2010) It's a one man show. *Mental Health Today*, March, 32-33

Whitwell D (1999) The myth of recovery from mental illness. *Psychiatric Bulletin*, **23**, 10, 621-622

Chapter 4

Recovery and Personal Narratives
Dr Glenn Roberts

'Stories matter. Many stories matter. Stories have been used to dispossess and malign but stories can also be used to empower and humanise. Stories can be used to break the dignity of a people but stories can also be used to repair that broken dignity.'

[Chimamanda Adichie]

The significance of stories

As a master story-teller and author, speaking about the value of stories, Adichie can convincingly assert that stories matter and offers a cautionary perspective that the potency of stories is such that they can result in both healing or harm. In the compelling speech from which this quote is drawn (hear it at Adichie, 2009) she tells a story about stories and achieves extraordinary impact within the 18 minute presentation. She draws us in by speaking of her life and circumstances and her development as a person as well as a writer. Her purpose is to illustrate how allowing particular stories to rise above all others into a dominant position gives the impression that there is only one story about someone or something, which then becomes a 'single story', a stereotype that restricts an appreciation of individuality, diversity, richness and complexity and instead provides a focus for prejudice, stigma and discrimination. Her method is an illustration of the power of stories to wrap the generalities of principle and theory in the specifics of human experience. In this we are humanised, in this we become people, in this we become people who belong together and form a society in which stories can be shared and held in common. Restoration of a central focus on a personal perspective through personal stories is something this book is about too.

Our recent history has been to trivialise story, 'it's only a story', where 'telling stories' amounts almost to telling lies and narrative contributions and personal testimony are placed at the bottom of the evidence hierarchy used in compiling guidelines. These sort of concerns about the depersonalised nature of our guidelines, our standard texts and training materials led one observer to note the complete absence of any qualitative studies from the whole of the first year's publication of the *British Journal of Evidence Based Mental Health* and comment on the "enormous gap between our empirical knowledge base and the information that patients need and want," (Szatmari, 1999). As one person with a schizophrenia diagnosis said, "I have read a lot about schizophrenia but the books have very little to say about how to recover... It's all rather depressing." This has to, and is, changing (Roberts, 2000).

Part of this change has arisen from concerns about how peculiar it is that studies and teaching in human services and the helping professions had progressively excluded an emphasis on the experience and lived-lives of the people intended to be so served and helped. The theologian and hospital chaplain Stanley Hauerwas (1993) spoke of the need "to restore the human subject at the centre – the suffering afflicted frightened human subject – we must deepen our case history to a narrative or tale, only then do we have a who, as well as a what, a patient – a person, in relation to a disease...it is only within a life story that illness has a meaningful place."

The psychologist Miller Mair (1988) sees just about all of human psychology as circling around story and narrativity, "Stories are habitations. We live in and through stories. They conjure worlds. Stories inform life. They hold us together and keep us apart. We inhabit the great stories of our culture." And deployment of this artfulness, this creativity, discovery and development of stories-to-live-by seems to both accompany and may constitute an essential element in healing and recovery.

Narrative foundations of the recovery movement

The roots of the present recovery movement have been traced back to compassionate humanism and creative activism of people working for human and disability rights over the last couple of hundred years (Davidson et al, 2010). Nearly a decade ago a summary of mental health policy was published as *The Journey to Recovery: The Government's Vision for Mental Health Care* (DH, 2001). This began by observing that, "Historically people with mental illness were often not expected to recover", but went on to express a hope that, "...services of the future will talk as much about recovery as they do about symptoms and illness ...the vast majority have real prospects of recovery – if they are supported by appropriate services, driven by the right values and attitudes."

Over the last ten years there has been a gathering interest and sharpening focus on 'recovery' as the guiding purpose of mental health and social care services (Repper and Perkins, 2003, CSIP et al, 2007, Roberts and Hollins, 2007). There is increasing recognition that what has become the dominant approach of traditional services – focusing on getting better from symptoms, problems, difficulties and disorders, i.e. clinical recovery, does not necessarily enable people to go forward into a valued pattern of life and living with or without ongoing problems, i.e. personal recovery (Slade, 2009). Personal recovery centres on recovering a life and pattern of living that a person values. It is about having a place in society and gaining or regaining the rights and responsibilities common to all citizens. Hence, alongside the continuing production of evidence-based treatment guides, there has been a growing emphasis on the importance of choice, opportunity, hope, self-determination, social inclusion and personalisation as overarching mediators of wellbeing (Boardman et al, 2010, National Mental Health Development Unit, 2010). Many of these factors are prominent in individual stories of personal recovery and thematic analysis of anthologies of such stories have provided the foundation of the international recovery movement (for example in USA, Ralph, 2005, New Zealand, Lapsley et al, 2002 and Scotland, Scottish Recovery Network, 2010a).

Some have worried that talking about personal recovery for people with long term ('chronic') conditions is an unacceptable distortion of ordinary language that usually associates 'recovery' with 'cure' (Oyebode, 2004). Some have disputed professional and organisational interest in adopting the recovery approach, seeing it as an attempted takeover or 'colonisation' of something that belongs to the service user movement (Social Perspectives Network, 2007, MIND, 2008). Some have worried quite appropriately that organisations, teams and services will see merit in superficially relabelling themselves as 'recovery-focused' without engaging with the fundamental challenges that are needed for it to be meaningful, as described in *Implementing Recovery: A Methodology for Organisational Change* (SCMH, 2010). To a degree this has been answered by recognition that recovery fundamentally 'belongs' to the person themselves, that services cannot 'recover' anyone but they can do much to help or hinder. To a greater degree a recurring emphasis on the value of learning from personal stories serves an essential function of maintaining a central focus on personal perspectives.

By the time *New Horizons* was formulated as a guide for the current decade (DH 2009, p. 7) there was a clear emphasis that "services to treat and care for people with mental health problems will be accessible to all who need them, based on the best available evidence and focused on recovery, as defined in discussion with the service user." But we are not yet familiar with having such discussions and when we do, we may be in for some surprises.

"I have recovered from schizophrenia. If that statement surprises you – if you think schizophrenia is a lifelong brain disease that cannot be escaped – you have been misled by a cultural misapprehension that needlessly imprisons millions under the label of mental illnesses." So begins Daniel Fisher's (2001) robust autobiographical rallying call in the *Washington Post*. In doing so he appropriates the unarguable authority of personal experience, in effect he is asserting 'I am the evidence' for the reality of personal recovery from schizophrenia. And he is not the first, nor is he alone.

Jan Wallcraft (in MIND, 2008) has argued that the recovery approach was pioneered and developed by people who used services. This approach initially came to prominence in the 1980s and 1990s with the publication of a number of influential articles in the form of first person narratives tracking the journeys of service users such as those by Lovejoy (1984), Unzicker (1989) and Leete (1989). These demonstrated that many people who had been written off by mental health professionals were successfully finding ways of living full, satisfying and contributing lives despite experiencing mental distress. Their foundational stories ignited vision and interest so as to change the climate of hope and expectation around severe mental health problems from pessimistic prognostication to knowing from experience that you simply don't know what is possible until you try, and the results are often a good deal more than you dared to hope for or expect.

In a field that has been characterised by hopelessness there is a sore need for hope (Perkins, 2006), which is a significant aspect of what this book is all about. The stories it contains are an excellent preparation for some of the meaningful discussions between us all that lie ahead.

Beware of 'The Recovery Model' as a single story

As lead on recovery for the Royal College of Psychiatrists I've sought to stimulate the interest of people in my own profession about personal recovery for some years. This has given me the opportunity to contribute to major publications such as *A Common Purpose* (CSIP et al, 2007) and debates such as the MINDThink seminar on *The Life and Times of a Supermodel* (2008). But a pivotal issue that arose in these and many other settings is the problem of considering recovery as a 'model'.

This came up again for me recently when, in response to my wish to follow up on the commitment the Royal College of Psychiatrists has made to "ensure that training for psychiatrists promotes the recovery approach" (RCPsych, 2008), I was approached by the Examinations Unit at the College. The Unit asked if I would work with them to produce some questions 'focusing on the recovery model'. On the face of it I should have been pleased but instead it set off an alarm, for a good exam question would be, 'Why is recovery not a model?'

It is of course possible, and to a limited degree helpful, to make models of the recovery process and these tend to vary with the model makers such as the linear, staged model of Retta Andresen and colleagues (2006) and the associated Stages of Recovery Index (STORI) or the more interactive and dynamic picture drawn up by Ruth Ralph (2005) from qualitative analysis of people's recovery narratives. But recovery itself is not a model. The map is not the land. Recovery is more appropriately understood as an approach, orientation, hope, goal, philosophy, ambition and achievement, but not a model.

There is an interesting relationship between models of recovery and personal stories. So for example measures of personal, practice and service progression in recovery as described in the Recovery Outcome Star (MHPF, 2010), Scottish Recovery Indicator (Scottish Recovery Network, 2010b) and Developing a Recovery Enhancing Environment Measure (DREEM, Dinniss et al, 2007) have all been developed from extensive review of stories of personal recovery, searching methodically for common threads and themes (Ridgeway, 2000). But it is absolutely pivotal when entering personally upon a road of recovery to recognise that it is a journey of discovery, and what has been described as, "an uncharted, unpredictable, and personal journey" (Sheehan, 2002).

To consider recovery as a model is to risk making of it a 'single story', which can only shackle or fail. It is a long way from Pat Deegan's foundational description of recovery as "a journey of the heart" (1996). It follows that however much we may wish there was one, there cannot be a handbook on 'how to be a recovery-oriented practitioner' and there can never really be a 'recovery therapy'. Although there are many books and courses about personal recovery, as well as therapeutic skills and treatments of all kinds that can be useful to people in recovery, these are just the tools, and increasingly they are used under the direction or control of the person themselves.

Recovery is therefore not something you can give or do to someone else so much as something you can support people in finding out for themselves. There is no better way of understanding what personal recovery means and how it is achieved than through stories from people who have been and are in recovery themselves, told in their own words and their own ways, representing their individuality, creativity and unique achievement.

Stories and stigma

Madness (psychosis) has long been associated with confusion, fear and fascination. The person in the street may think they know a lot about madness, but much of what they know is wrong. Of the great variety of human experiences there are few that are so likely to be met with misunderstanding, prejudice and stigma as psychosis. The contributors to this valuable book have therefore broken with one of society's last taboos in coming forward and offering us their personal perspective on the struggle for recovery with psychosis.

There is also a casual, untrue and destructive assumption that if someone has had an episode of psychosis, had a 'mental breakdown', or gone mad, they have passed through a one-way door and are forever-after a different sort of person: a 'mad-man' or woman, 'schizophrenic', or crazy. This binding together, conflation, of people with their health problems such as to lose sight of the person-with-a-problem is to alienate, to deny someone the social status as 'one of us' and instead mark them out, stigmatise, regard them as 'other'. The major investigation into social exclusion (ODPM, 2004), found that people with severe mental health problems said that their experience of stigma, prejudice and discrimination could be a greater source of suffering than the problems themselves. These observations have been both a terrible indictment of social attitudes in the general population and also the touchstone and inspiration of a move to take effective action (Boardman et al, 2010) and recognise that it is time to end mental health discrimination (www.time-to-change.org.uk).

There have been many attempts to 'do something' about public perceptions of mental distress and illness though few have shown much success, but one of the most reliable methods has been through personal encounter, meeting with and hearing from people with problems and hearing their stories. This almost inevitably means seeing a person in a context, not just as a case or a problem, and hearing people speak about their lives illustrates how things can change for better and worse over time. There are obvious difficulties in organising such encounters and complex costs involved, including to the person recurrently telling and reliving the story of their difficulties. Recorded stories may be the next best thing, and stories of personal recovery have been used in all kinds of settings and media. A pivotal experience for me was coming across Julie Leibrich's (1999) inspirational book *A Gift of Stories* which was developed as part of a national anti-stigma campaign in New Zealand. I immediately bought six copies and made it available to people I was working with. One of them gained hope and strength by reading these stories of personal recovery to her hostile and demeaning voices.

The people within this book have taken a bold step, to struggle with complexity of their experience and develop it into a coherent, engaging and helpful story, as a gift to others. The makers of this book have taken the further step to draw these individual contributions together to offer a restorative bridge across a whole range of contradictions. In particular that people can and do recover from psychosis and that this most confusing and enigmatic experience can be sufficiently understood by the person travelling through it to be caught in a story.

Narrative foundations of personal recovery: The search for a story to live by

The need for narrative seems to hold true for people in all kinds of extreme circumstances. Terry Waite, one of the Beirut hostages, spoke about how he coped with his prolonged experience of solitary confinement, "I soon realised that if I was to survive, it was essential to maintain a strong inner life. I needed to tell myself stories. In telling myself the story of my life I was maintaining a life line with reality I had known and lived...when I eventually emerged all I wanted was a pencil and notebook. The book was already written in my mind. One eminent reviewer described the book as being 'egocentric'. He quite failed to see that the writer was attempting to hang onto identity, because the threat of dissolving into madness was ever-present."

So it appears that we can use our narrativity, our storytelling abilities, to hold onto sanity and protect ourselves from adversity and as such it is part of resilience. We can also use our capacity to make sense out of confusion within psychosis by attributing meaning to experience. It is therefore possible to understand many of the symptoms of psychosis as creative adaptations, coping mechanisms, to more threatening experiences and more complex dissolutions of meaning. If we are serious in seeking to understand madness (Roberts, 2006) we may therefore need to consider how people cope and adapt by finding meaning in, with and through their psychotic experiences. Part of the complexity of recovery (see below) is in retracing, rescinding and unravelling some of these complex and creative adaptations.

All the contributors to this book can and do speak from considerable personal experience. Many look back over years and can offer a considered reflection on the journey so far, good and bad from the vantage of the present. So how has that happened? Many will tell you themselves in these pages but it seems that the road to recovery is often accompanied by a process of narrative transformation. As we progress in a process of personal healing we develop and redevelop the story of our lives so as to have an account that make sense to us and supports our life and living. Through sharing and finding a place for our story with others we are connected and are able to access shared stories that hold together groups and movements. We become social beings through sharing stories.

But it also seems that how we make sense of our experience is transformed as we travel through that experience. Shery Mead's (2005) approach to peer support has a framework in which she invites people to think about their 'world view' and 'how they know what they know'. Having joined in group exercises and training led by Mead I have been impressed at the changes that follow her asking people to pair up and tell their stories to one another. Many of these are initially stories of symptoms, treatment, diagnosis and of things done to people, including hospitalisation. Having heard these descriptions she then asked us to do the same thing again, but try to avoid clinical language, and tell their story from a personal perspective. Something different happened, people spoke about their relationships and circumstances, their loves and losses, their hopes and fears for the future and what they had, could and wanted to do.

I attended these workshops with a colleague who had a much-rehearsed story of his service user experiences that was associated with his valued role as a service user trainer. He was used to starting his story with something along the lines of, "I was first diagnosed schizophrenic when I was 19 and have since had 12 admissions under the Mental Health Act." Following us both participating in this exercise he gave it another go, "I was 19 and working in x when the shit hit the fan ...", and was very pleased by a growing sense of coming back into his own skin. He – we – were invited to engage in a process of narrative transformation, from telling a predominantly clinical story to a personal one and in doing so we also came to consider how peers can support one another to find themselves, to find their own story, their lived autobiography. This shift, this transition, could be taken to document recovery-in-process, but as a personal achievement, as a shift of perspective and of the story you tell yourselves and live in, it may of itself constitute recovery-in-progress. It seems important to be aware of the risk of getting trapped in a story and instead to live with the hope and possibility of your story shifting and changing as does your perspective on your life. When you are actually at the bottom of a deep hole your view of the world is restricted to a narrow circle of the sky above you and all you want is to get out. But as you climb up and out of the hole, the breadth of the vision above you expands when you reach the surface and you are surrounded by possibilities and face other restrictions but, in principle, can go in any direction and do anything you please.

Some recovery support tools explicitly engage in reflection on the language we use and the plots we use to tell the story of our lives. For example Ron

Coleman's (2000) personal planning tool presented in the book *Working to Recovery* includes major sections that invite the user to record their story as well as their 'mental health career'. This is one of a series of work books which are collectively titled *Victim to Victor* (2000). In the introduction it states that, "There is a need for another kind of language. A more positive and enabling language that acknowledges the potential of recovery, respects the desire to stop being a victim and to become a victor of your experience and doesn't stand in the way when you seek to find your routes to recovery."

I've been struck by how people in recovery tell different stories about their lives and experiences as they progress. Mead has gone so far as to suggest that a good recovery outcome measure would be one that sensitively represented these shifts in the story that people tell about their lives. And it follows that a future skill for recovery-oriented practitioners may be to stimulate and support this process of narrative transformation. Familiarity with a wide range of personal stories such as are offered here could provide a good foundation.

The problem of diagnosis and the risk of losing the plot

Many people, including perhaps most of the people in this book, have struggled with diagnosis, and it is complex. Without diagnosis they wouldn't be in this book for it is a book of personal stories gathered around a diagnostic concept, psychosis. But many would also not be in this book if they had not moved on from diagnosis, if they had not recovered from 'psychosis' as a 'single story' that dominated their lives and eclipsed their identity, and recovered for themselves a sense of personhood, which may be the hallmark of recovery (Anthony, 2004).

Diagnosis, in my view, is greatly misunderstood and misused, but not in the way you may at first think. Many take a view that diagnosis is simply wrong, a bad if not abusive practice. And yet if asked more carefully they do not really have these strong views about diagnosis as a whole but rather as specific diagnoses. Foremost amongst those that are disliked and problematic is 'schizophrenia'. This is a word, a name given to a mysterious condition which has historically being laden down with pessimism, fear and stigma. It is also one of the more common diagnoses held by the international founders of the recovery movement.

The issue I would hesitatingly raise here is that diagnosis, used well, is about pattern recognition, and that's all. It gives a name to a pattern of experience, a what. It doesn't and cannot give a who, or a how. It doesn't offer comment or understanding of the person themselves or what preceded the experience or caused it. Neither does diagnosis in itself offer a clear prediction of the future health prospects, prognosis, for individuals, which, for mental health conditions, is and always has been enormously variable. So diagnosis is not and shouldn't be a 'single story', and yet all too often it can become so and it's no wonder that people who have been given such diagnostic assessments are so often reluctant to accept them. In being willing to identify themselves personally with the psychosis diagnosis, the contributors to this book should be congratulated and celebrated; they are pioneers and adventurers of the new way of doing things.

Personal perspectives illustrate the complexities of recovery

I have previously observed that recovery is work and often hard work. Apart from the struggle to restore loss or damage to the practicalities of everyday life, the struggle for understanding and acceptance on the journey in and out of psychosis takes many people into one of the most profound encounters with meaning and purpose it is possible to have.

Karl Jaspers (1963), from the vantage point of meticulous observation stated that in his view, "Extreme psychotic states offer a human parable...patients see into the depths which do not belong so much to their illness as themselves as individuals with their own historical truth... in psychotic reality we find an abundance of content representing fundamental problems in philosophy... the philosopher in us cannot but be fascinated by this extraordinary reality and to feel its challenge." But these philosophical fascinations also represent for some the complexity of what people have found or created within their psychotic experiences and may lose on recovery.

Some of this complexity has been illustrated by the artist William Kurelek (1927-1977) who as a patient in the Maudsley Hospital in 1953 painted his famous evocation of madness, *The Maze*. This autobiographical image is a surreal fantasy of the events and inhabitants of various compartments of his mind depicted in a cross-section of his head divided into an inescapable maze. It is a startling, fascinating and justly famous image. Far less known is the image he painted after his recovery and returning to his family in Canada, *Out of the Maze*. Here is a simple pastoral landscape in which he has pictured himself having a picnic with his wife and four small children. It is uneventful and calm but rather sparse and empty and as a biographical note includes a small image in one corner of an empty skull. This is not a famous, much reproduced or celebrated image and these two autobiographical images stand in stark contrast to one another. However they raise complex questions concerning the transition and transformative journey from madness to sanity, illness to wellness, and where you, anyone, would rather be. These curious pictures (both of which can be seen in Howard, 2001) can be taken as a double image, a diptych, holding the complexity of competing experiences, emotions, thoughts, perceptions and beliefs associated with what is otherwise a healing transition, the journey to recovery, which includes loss, and all that is caught in between.

The Maze is amazing, but the hypnotic fascination with our fears and fantasies represents both a fulfilment and a trap. The 'comforts of madness' (Sayers, 1989) remain exquisitely uncomfortable. For some, becoming sane, recovery, engages with a not easily resolved dilemma. The paradoxical possibility that there may be pain in recovery needs to be carefully held in mind by supporters if they are not to lose connection and compassion for those going through this most difficult of transitions. Many have commented on the courage it takes to face reality and we should be grateful to the contributors within this book who have made that courageous step in facing their own reality and through their stories enable us to see the reality of illness and recovery in psychosis more clearly too.

Restor(y)ing professional perspectives: The future skills of a recovery-oriented practitioner

Earlier in this book Frank Holloway evokes an awareness of the monumental pile of information that has accumulated around the topic of psychosis over the last hundred years and helpfully and successfully summarises an orthodox answer to the question 'What is psychosis?'. But he also notes that even after mining this mountain of words in the search for understanding psychosis there continues to be a mystery concerning its fundamental cause such that, "At the moment at least, psychiatrists and other mental health professionals depend on the story that the patient and their carers provide and an examination of the person's mental state: from these a diagnosis can be made."

Our basic understanding arises from listening, soliciting, facilitating, ordering, clarifying, summarizing and interpreting this story and refracting our observations through our knowledge and understanding to arrive at a diagnosis or diagnostic formulation and the risk is that we stop there. Sartre's critique (in Sims, 1988) that, "Psychiatry is too quickly satisfied when it throws light on the general structures of delusions and does not seek to comprehend the individual, concrete content of the psychosis", went unheeded for many years apart from the esoteric depths of analytical speculation and the anarchic elevation of psychedelic theorists. More recently, through the increasingly accepted perspective of 'voice hearers' (Romme and Escher, 2002) and the discoveries of cognitive theorists and practitioners (Rhodes and Jakes,

2009) there has been a gradual acceptance of the possibility that in some metaphoric, thematic or symbolic fashion, people experiencing psychosis continue to speak of their lives and their life experience and even in the depths of madness people are not speaking nonsense, although what people say and believe can be very difficult to understand (Roberts, 2006).

Some are uncomfortable or even angrily rejecting of their experience being reformatted into a diagnostic formulation. However others are helped and oriented by knowing that for all the unique qualities of their experience there are also recognisable similarities with the experience of others which forms a pattern that can be given a name, which then offers a key to a door of knowledge and connection.

However, as I've described, any diagnostic assessment can only offer a name to the pattern of distress which falls considerably short of understanding the person who is having that experience and of a great many issues that are important in their recovery: their strengths, preferences and circumstance and what it all means for them. If we do not work hard to put any diagnostic assessment into a biographical and social context we will have seriously misunderstood what is needed to support people in recovery. For as Klienman (1988, p. 180) observed, "Once the patient's biography becomes part of the care, the possibility that therapy will dehumanise the patient, stripping him of what is unique to his illness experience becomes much less likely," (see also, Strauss, 1994).

One of the core characteristics of countries and services around the world that are developing a commitment to recovery has been in grounding their developments on a review of what matters to people as represented in their personal recovery stories (Lapsley et al, 2002, Scottish Recovery Network, 2010a). There is also an emerging interest in gathering personal stories within a service context, in effect 'this is who we are and what happens here' for example in first episode psychosis services (EPPIC, 2000), and forensic services (South West London and St George's, 2010). One of the key things learned from these stories is not only about the content of people's experiences, what they are going through, sponsoring empathy and compassion, but also an understanding of the process they are going through and what helps and hinders personal recovery. Local anthologies of recovery stories thereby hold potential to become talismanic tales, stories that carry a collective memory of the people who have come before you, are doing well and offer a sense of companionship and fellow travelling as to how to cope and how to progress.

As a clinician I share with other clinicians an interest in evidence-based treatment. After all, would you really want a treatment for which there was no evidence of it being effective? But as a recovery-oriented clinician I'm also interested in what people find works for themselves in terms of supporting their recovery. This may or may not include 'treatment' but will almost certainly include much else. And collections of personal recovery stories are full of people describing these discoveries. The reader may be introduced to strategies or interesting opportunities that resonate with them and also may want to try. They will be introduced to many examples of how people have become active in their own recovery and through enquiry and experimentation discover what works for them, which in turn suggests that you too can discover what helps you recover.

Stories from founders of the recovery movement and many of those within this book make it abundantly clear that progress in personal recovery is not dependant on getting a perfect service. Many describe poor, or worse, experience of services and their determination to recover despite this. It is a salutary and humbling realisation for practitioners that services cannot 'recover' anyone, but can provide the supports, stimulus and preconditions of recovery that make it more likely that people can successfully embark on their own recovery. The practitioners' contribution at best is only half the picture – the other is dependent on how people engage with their own recovery and how they use the helps and supports around them.

It follows that the desired outcome for those entering a 'recovery-focused service' is not in becoming 'empowered service users' but people who are able and hopeful about getting on with their lives on their own terms, with or without mental health services. Mary O'Hagan has drawn attention to the possibility of peer education on personal recovery (2009), although at present in the UK this is an aspirational development for the future – for which this book and those like it will be foundational texts. Likewise the future recovery-oriented practitioner will not primarily be good at 'treatment' but with skills of successfully supporting people in developing self-directed care and self-management and have skills to understand and enable people to work with and develop their personal stories and draw on the potentially profound benefits of peer support.

Cautionary notes: Anything real casts a shadow

Hope cannot be securely based on fantasy or on part pictures that screen out the bits we do not like or want. Real hope, the sort of hope you can live by, rather than just be buoyed up and feel good about, needs to arise from a rich blend of optimism and realism. This is a challenging and sometimes painful path that many of the contributors here are leading us on. In this there is a dilemma. On the one hand we want to push back the pervasive pessimism that has so often overshadowed our attitudes and expectations for people with psychosis. But on the other, if we are to offer genuine hope, hope that works in the real world, we do need to consider the shadows too, for undoubtedly psychosis is one of the most burdensome and challenging experiences that comes to people. And many people and their families know only too well of the sadness, fear and confusion it represents. This too is part of 'lived experience' and to avoid it is to risk being superficial and naive. Shadows give depth.

All the people in this book have survived profound, disruptive and complex disturbances in their lives but through their personal stories have significantly reset the frame of our considerations. Future study of 'psychosis' should be about 'people who experience psychosis', and be as interested in how people adapt and cope and manage these experiences as in clarifying the evidence in support of treatment effectiveness. Real world 'outcomes' will depend on a combination of both.

My chief focus in this chapter has been on how stories can connect – but as Adichie emphasised at the beginning they can also disconnect. To stay connected with people, families and practitioners who struggle with the dark and sometimes tragic realities that also characterise the sufferings of severe mental illness we must also make space and keep a door open on those other stories. For some recovery lies beyond surviving such experiences, or surviving the experiences of others - with grief. It is the hope of this book and of the many other contributions to recovery approaches everywhere to lighten that darkness and hold hope for better futures. But even in these most difficult times it is important not to underestimate the value and power of understanding and preserving a personal perspective.

Greg Bottoms (2001) has written with honesty and great sensitivity about his experience as the brother of someone with a schizophrenia diagnosis and of the value of understanding. He comments on the alienating detachment of clinical texts, "When you read about schizophrenia, you can begin to believe it is disembodied, abstract, simply out there, not actually having to do with human beings, with teenagers and young adults, with families." He describes the confusion of being given disconnected scraps of information from different practitioners, "Doctors told my parents different, divergent stories that intersected at points but never made a coherent narrative." Nonetheless he felt the struggle for understanding was almost life saving as he struggled to cope with his brother's psychosis, "With sympathy the early stages of schizophrenia are a massive burden; without sympathy and understanding, without love and care even in the face of the strangest behaviours, schizophrenia is a wrecking ball."

He points to the major concern about how our impersonal and professionalised perspectives can detach us from forming relationships with individuals and families in a helpful and sensitive way. Greenhalgh and Hurwitz (1998) spoke about this difficulty across the whole of modern medicine which they felt "at its most arid ... lacks a metric for existential qualities such as inner hurt, despair, hope, grief and moral pain which frequently accompany, and often indeed constitute, the illnesses from which people suffer." This led to them making a convincing case for reintroducing a narrative perspective to medical teaching and learning and making a claim for 'narrative-based medicine' emphasizing stories and qualitative dimensions as a complementary perspective to the more numerical and statistical 'evidence-based medicine'.

We must also take care not to break connection with those who are currently struggling deeply in the dark who can feel excluded and rebuffed by what can seem inaccessible hope. When our collection of reflections on personal recovery in Devon, *Beyond the Storms* was published (Davidson and Lynn, 2009) we made sure it was freely available to people on our residential rehabilitation unit. Some liked it, valued it and found it a support for their own recovery, but one person said she couldn't read it. "It wasn't very realistic", she explained, it wasn't about people like her, she couldn't find herself within its covers, it was too hopeful, life seemed to be too simple and successful for those authors compared to her experience. She found it distressing, alienating. A year later the picture has changed and so has her sense of connection with having hope for herself and being comfortable in the company of others whose lives are progressing. For a long time professional staff were really the only people in her life and it was part of their work to be 'holders of hope', but where do they get such hope from themselves? It cannot be sustained if it is only a matter of rather stubbornly clinging to some form of unrealistic optimism – but it can be upheld with conviction where staff have heard and seen such changes for themselves.

It is in the nature of stories to touch, inspire, move, motivate, illuminate, guide, illustrate and offer a basis for hope and identification...'if you then maybe me too'. But we must also touch on the darker ways in which stories can influence, as they also entice, seduce, deceive, confuse and enchant and are the stuff of advertisements and propaganda. The power of stories to beguile has been elegantly demonstrated in studies using experimental drama where children were far more likely to express willingness to give money and even say they would donate their body tissues to needy causes if the need were presented in the form of an emotive story rather than simply through a presentation of the facts. The researcher concluded that "seeing a person's misfortune in the frame of their personal story increases engagement in the misfortunes and readiness to help this person" (Trzebinski, 2005). This apparently universal principle in human psychology can clearly be used for good or ill. The malleability of information in persuasive stories is one of the reasons they have all but vanished from medical journals in favour of evidence based medicine. It is clear that we do primarily understand one another through narrative, and sometimes we are quite wrong. Hence the perennial tension between the arts and sciences in searching for meaning and understanding. It is a creative and often healing process for people to find a way of reconsidering the meanings they are living with but the very flexibility and changeability of stories that gives them life and purpose is a basis for concern in those who look for reliable and unchanging facts.

Science searches for resilient and reproducible observations and results and naturally worries about the falsehoods that can arise if knowledge is gathered from convincing stories rather than investigation and verification.

Creative expression belongs with the arts, systematic analysis with the sciences and they easily fall out with one another. Richard Smith (2002), a past editor of the *British Medical Journal* wrote a fascinating defence of the value of the arts in relieving human suffering and supporting health and healing. "Health has to do with adaptation and acceptance. We will be sick, suffer loss and hurt, even die. Health is not to do with avoiding these givens, but with accepting them, even making sense of them...If health is about adaptation, understanding, and acceptance, then the arts may be more potent that anything that medicine has to offer." But for me this tension cannot legitimately be resolved by competition or setting one form of description up against another in a hierarchy. I feel it is best resolved by a respectful realisation that both are of great value, each has its place, each is better suited for a particular task and taken together they add up to far more than either does separately. For me the contemporary practitioner is best seated on a three-legged stool, supported by evidence, narrative and ethics i.e. numbers, stories and values. He or she must still enter relationships, negotiate and make judgements, but is all the more securely placed to do so if well supported by all three.

The close of one and the beginning of many others

We've seen by many turns that stories are serious things and are primarily how we make and transact meaning. Stories inspire and guide through echo and resonance rather than offering rules and protocols. They offer insight and understanding and can be iconic, offering images and evocations that draw you in to see, and see through, to what is behind and beyond. Stories, characteristically, have a beginning, middle and end. They carry a rhythm of temporal succession and flow and carry you along, and they describe people moving along in their lives and lend energy and momentum to others too. The most compelling are described as gripping or 'page turners' and the process of arriving at a story of personal experience and recovery is about people taking back authority over their own lives and turning the pages and chapters of their lived autobiography. This collection of personal stories of recovery from psychosis will undoubtedly be of value to people with similar experience and beyond that offers companionship and hope for people using services and staff alike, demonstrating as it does that the guiding ethic of health and social care services should be in putting people first.

But reading about stories is no substitute for the stories themselves and the main point and purpose of this book is about to follow. In writing these notes I've leaned heavily on the views, opinions and experiences I've gathered over a professional lifetime and although I've cited many others to extend or support my argument, this remains inevitably and unavoidably a personal viewpoint. In closing I would not want to claim any more authority than 'this is how I see it', and to emphasise that, as with personal recovery, the most important realisations you have will be those you discover for yourself - good luck.

References

Adichie, C (2009) The danger of a single story. www.ted.com/talks/lang/eng/chimamanda_adichie_the_danger_of_a_single_story.html accessed June 11th 2010

Andresen, R, Caputi, P, Oades, L (2006) The Stages of Recovery Instrument: Development of a measure of recovery from serious mental illness. *Australian and New Zealand Journal of Psychiatry*, **40**: 972-980

Anthony, W (2004) The principle of personhood: The field's transcendent principle. *Psychiatric Rehabilitation Journal*, **27**, 205

Boardman, J, Currie, A, Killaspy, H, Mezey, G (2010) *Social Inclusion and Mental Health*. RCPsych Publications: London

Bottoms, G (2001) *Angel-head: My brother's descent into madness*. Headline Book

Publishing: London

Coleman, R, Baker, P, Taylor, K (2000) Working to recovery: Victim to victor III. *A guide to mental wellbeing. A personal planning tool.* Handsell Publishing: Gloucester

CSIP, RCPsych, SCIE (2007) *A common purpose: Recovery in future mental health services.* Social Care Institute for Excellence: London

Davidson, L, Lynn, L (2009) *Beyond the storms: Reflections on mental health recovery in Devon.* Available free from www.recoverydevon.co.uk

Davidson, L, Rakfeldt, J, Strauss, J (2010) *The roots of the recovery movement in psychiatry.* Wiley-Blackwell: Chichester

Deegan, P (1996) Recovery as a journey of the heart. *Psychiatric Rehabilitation Journal,* **19**, 3, 91-97

Department of Health (2001) *The journey to recovery – the Government's vision for mental health care.* Department of Health: London

Department of Health (2009) *New Horizons: a shared vision for mental health.* Department of Health: London

Dinniss, S, Roberts, G, Hounsell, J, Webb, R (2007) A user-led assessment of the recovery orientation of a rehabilitation service using DREEM: The Developing Recovery Enhancing Environments Measure. *Psychiatric Bulletin,* **31**, 124-127

EPPIC (2000) *Trips and Journeys. Personal accounts of early psychosis.* Early Psychosis Prevention and Intervention Centre: Melbourne

Fisher, D B (2001) We've been misled by the drug industry. *Washington Post,* 19 August, p. B3. Also at www.power2u.org

Greenhalgh, T, Hurwitz, B (1998) Why study narrative? In *Narrative Based Medicine* (Eds T Greenhalgh, B Huwitz). BMJ Books: London

Hauerwas, S (1993) *Naming the silences: God, Medicine and the problem of suffering.* T&T Clark: Edinburgh

Howard, R (2001) Psychiatry in Pictures. *British Journal of Psychiatry*, **179**, A18. http://bjp.rcpsych.org/cgi/reprint/179/5/0.pdf

Jaspers, K (1963) *General Psychopathology*, 309. Trans. J Hoenig & J W Hamiliton. Manchester University Press. Republished 1998 by Johns Hopkins University Press: Balitimore

Kleinman, A (1988) *The illness narratives: Suffering, healing and the human condition*. Basic Books: New York

Lapsley, H, Waimarie, L N, Black, R (2002) *Kia Mauri Tau!: Narratives of recovery from disabling mental health problems*. Mental Health Commission: Wellington

Leete, E (1989) How I perceive and manage my illness. *Schizophrenia Bulletin*, **8**, 605–609

Leibrich, J (1999) *A gift of stories: Discovering how to deal with mental illness*. University of Otago Press: Dunedin

Lovejoy, M (1984) Recovery from schizophrenia: A personal Odyssey. *Hospital and Community Psychiatry*, **35**, 809–812

Mair, M (1988) Psychology as storytelling. *International Journal of Personal Construct Psychology*, **1**, 125-138

Mead, S (2005) *Intentional peer support: An alternative approach*. Plainfield, NH: Shery Mead Consulting. (see also www.mentalhealthpeers.com)

Mental Health Providers Forum (2010) Mental Health Recovery Star. http://www.outcomesstar.org.uk/mental-health/ accessed on 19th August, 2010

MIND (2008) *The life and times of a supermodel: The recovery paradigm for mental health*. MIND: London

National Mental Health Development Unit (2010) *Paths to personalisation in mental health*. London: National Mental Health Development Unit: London

Office of the Deputy Prime Minister (2004) Mental Health and Social Exclusion. www.cabinetoffice.gov.uk/media/cabinetoffice/social_exclusion_task_force/assets/publications_1997_to_2006/mh.pdf

O'Hagan, M (2009) *Recovery in progress: Future recovery-based services, descriptions, examples and evidence.* Available at www.recoverydevon.co.uk

Oyebode, F (2004) Invited commentary on The rediscovery of recovery: Open to all. *Advances in Psychiatric Treatment,* **10**, 48-9

Perkins, R (2006) First person: 'You need hope to cope'. Ch 7 in *Enabling recovery: The principles and practice of rehabilitation psychiatry,* Roberts, G, Davenport, S, Holloway, F, Tattan, T (Eds). Gaskell: London

Ralph, R (2005) Verbal definitions and visual models of recovery: Focus on the recovery model. Ch 6 in *Recovery in mental illness,* Ralph, R and Corrigan, P (Eds). American Psychological Association: Washington DC

Repper, J, Perkins, R (2003) *Social inclusion and recovery: A model for mental health practice.* Bailliere Tindall: London

Ridgeway, P A (2000) Re-storying psychiatric disability: Learning from first person narrative accounts of recovery. *Psychiatric Rehabilitation Journal,* **24**, 335–343

Rhodes, J, Jakes, S (2009) *Narrative CBT for psychosis.* Routledge: London

Roberts, G A (2000) Narrative and severe mental illness: What place do stories have in an evidence-based world? *Advances in Psychiatric Treatment,* **6**, 432-441

Roberts, G (2006) Understanding madness. Ch 7 in *Enabling recovery: The principles and practice of rehabilitation psychiatry,* Roberts, G, Davenport, S, Holloway, F, Tattan, T (Eds). Gaskell: London

Roberts, G, Hollins, S (2007) Recovery: Our common purpose? *Advances in Psychiatric Treatment,* **13**, 397-399

Romme, M, Escher, S (2002) *Making sense of voices: A guide for mental health professionals working with voice hearers.* Mind Publications: London

Royal College of Psychiatrists (2008) *Fair deal for mental health,* p 27. Royal College of Psychiatrists: London www.rcpsych.ac.uk/campaigns/fairdeal.aspx

Sayers, P (1989) *The comforts of madness.* Sceptre: London

Sainsbury Centre for Mental Health (2010) *Implementing Recovery: A methodology for organisational change*. Sainsbury Center for Mental Health: London

Scottish Recovery Network (2010a) Narrative research project www.scottishrecovery. net/Narrative-Research-Project/narrative-research-project.html accessed 15.8.2010

Scottish Recovery Network (2010b) Scottish Recovery Indicator http://www. scottishrecoveryindicator.net/ accessed on 19th August, 2010

Sheehan, A (2002) Inspirations, a Photographic Record of Recovery. NIMHE: London

Sims, A (1988) *Symptoms in the mind: An introduction to descriptive psychopathology*. Elsevier: London:

Slade, M (2009) *Personal recovery and mental illness*. Cambridge University Press: Cambridge

Smith, R (2002) Editorial. Spend (slightly) less on health and more on the arts. *British Medical Journal*, 325, 1433-4

Social Perspectives Network (2007) *Whose recovery is it anyway?* Social Perspectives Network: London

South London and Maudsley NHS Foundation Trust (2010) *The Maze: A practical guide to the Mental Health Act 1983* (amended 2007). http://www. slam.nhs.uk/media/81045/maze%20leaflet.pdf

South West London and St George's (2010) *Our Stories: Moving on, recovery and wellbeing*. South West London and St George's NHS Trust: London

Strauss, J (1994) The person with schizophrenia as a person II: Approaches to the subjective and complex. *British Journal of Psychiatry*, **164** (Suppl. 23) 103-107

Szatmari, P (1999) Evidence-based child psychiatry and the two solitudes. *Evidence-Based Mental Health*, **2**, 6–7

Trzebinski, J (2005) Narratives and understanding other people. *Research in Drama Education*, **10**, 1, 19-29

Unzicker, R (1989) On my own: A personal journey through madness and re-emergence. *Psychosocial Rehabilitation Journal*, **13**, 70–77

The Voyce of Experience

Photo: Leonie Leckie

Chapter 5

The Voyce of Experience

Andrew Voyce, 59, of Bexhill, Sussex, is a veteran of the mental health system, having been treated for psychosis for over 35 years both as an inpatient and in the community. He credits reform in the management and medical treatment of people with psychosis as giving him a quality of life that has helped significantly in his recovery.

Background

I was born in 1951 in Park Royal Hospital, Willesden and grew up in Orpington, Kent. After passing the 11 plus I went onto Chislehurst and Sidcup Grammar School for Boys where I enjoyed school, particularly football and rugby, and got seven O levels and three A levels. At the age of 18 I went to Reading University to read Social Sciences where I majored in Politics. My main interest in politics at the time was the Marxist concept of alienation, which is where men and women are separated from their means of sustenance and shelter by what they do every day. When you separate people from the origin of their sustenance and shelter you get the division of labour that usually involves exploitation.

When I came across alienation in the university library I felt I had experienced it myself at my parents' building company. During the 1960s my parents helped to build, by today's standards, around £50m-worth of large detached luxury houses in Chislehurst, Orpington, Crowborough and Sevenoaks. They did quite well out of this company and my dad always had a brand new Jaguar. I'd started working there when I was about ten right up until my early twenties. They made me go down to the building site and put insulation in lofts and do odd jobs. I was told it was to help me earn pocket money but in hindsight I felt it was exploitation - I was helping my dad to buy his next Jaguar!

Transition towards illness

In my last year at school I'd had a bad motorbike accident and lost my right leg. This caused me lots of problems when I was at university – I had a prosthetic limb which was very uncomfortable and it was difficult to walk. I couldn't join in football and rugby and things like that which I'd previously enjoyed so I felt very alienated. In 1970 I'd got £2,000 compensation for losing my leg. You could get a terraced house in Reading for about £800 in those days and it was a great opportunity to do something with the money. But I didn't buy a house like I should have done; unfortunately I spent it on drugs and was exploited by drug dealers. Working people spend their whole lives trying to buy a terraced house in Reading, but I wasted the chance. This was a very bad pattern which I repeated after I was diagnosed with schizophrenia in my mid 30s.

At university I fell in with the wrong crowd - drop outs with long hair, long beards and body odour who smoked a lot and did as little as possible. I was getting stoned every single day and used to get a bit paranoid when I was on buses in Reading. Often I felt too paranoid to go to lectures and seminars. I didn't think I was ill, just that I was rejecting straight life and becoming a drop out. At the time we had a full employment economy and I felt I could drop out and drop back in again. This was something that people did at the time, because the level of unemployment then was very low by our standards today. There were always jobs on building sites and we also had the Welfare State, so I wasn't too worried about being unemployed. Eventually I went to see my tutor and told him I was cheesed off with the course and education in general, but really it was because my work rate had dropped off and I stopped attending lectures and seminars. So the tutor arranged for me to have a year off but I ended up having a two year sabbatical from university. The first year I still had a bit of compensation money left so I just spent that on pot. In the second year I went back to my parents and they said I could go out and carry sacks of cement on their building sites again, which I did. My leg was giving me a lot of trouble so in desperation I asked the university if I could come back and finish my final year. But I'd lost all academic spark and failed my final examinations, coming away with no degree. About six months later I was leading a fairly erratic lifestyle. I had one or two jobs in London but felt worthless because I'd failed my degree. At this time my parents got divorced and I went to stay with my father and his second wife

Realisation of problem

To complicate matters, I'd seen an advert in the London Evening Standard that said you could earn £100 a week driving a minicab, all you needed was a late model saloon and a current driving licence. I'd run out of money by this time, mainly because my father had taken some of it into his firm and I couldn't get it back, and I'd spent the rest on cannabis. So I borrowed £500 from my stepfather and mother to buy a Ford Cortina in the stupid hope that this advert was true. I did that for about four or five weeks and one week I worked about a hundred hours and got about £35! It was a con and I'd been done so I went back to my father in shame. I had been making a lot of unwise decisions and was very paranoid so he got me admitted to an asylum at Hellingly in East Sussex just before Christmas 1974. Initially I was in there for about two weeks but they discharged me saying there was nothing wrong with me. Despite this I think I was quite severely ill.

Crisis points

It was April 1975 and I was coming up for my twenty-fourth birthday when the hospital sent me back to live with my father. But I ended up having a fight with him and went off to live in this car which I still had. It was in the winter and I needed to run the engine to keep the heater going but I didn't have any money, so I began to fill up the car with petrol and drive off without paying. For about four or five weeks I drove all over the place - Scotland, Wales, Cornwall - filling up with petrol and driving off. I didn't eat very much at all, once or twice taking milk bottles from doorsteps or asking for fish and chips and running off without paying. Even in those days the police got you for stealing petrol, so eventually they caught me and sent me to Magistrate's Court where I got fined. I sold my car but didn't pay the fine, just went round doing the same thing in a hire car. I got arrested again for stealing petrol in the hire car at Reading of all places and the Magistrate gave me a two year probation order with the condition that I had mental health treatment at Hellingly where I had originally been. That time I was there for a number of months and it was the start of what I call my 'revolving door' time.

Contact with services and treatment

The second time I was admitted to Hellingly they diagnosed me with schizophrenia. It didn't really have any impact on me, because I didn't know anything about mental illness and just assumed it was something they did. But I was quite ill and had become very bothered by traffic. When I was driving around all over the place stealing petrol and the gauge got down towards zero, a whole load of traffic always suddenly seemed to appear around me. When I was about to drive out of the place where I'd stolen the petrol from there always seemed to be a whole load of traffic stopping me getting away. Coincidental things like that used to increase my paranoia and I half felt that this vast amount of traffic that kept appearing at awkward times was directed at me.

Between 1974 and 1991 I had about ten admissions to Hellingly and two admissions to Oakwood near Maidstone, Kent. This period was marked by administration of medication by injection – flupenthixol (Depixol) and fluphenazine (Modecate) – which produced horrendous side effects. It was a very humiliating procedure – I had to drop my trousers and have someone inject my backside with a concoction once a fortnight. For a week after my injection I would suffer a side effect called akathisia – from the Greek 'without sitting' – which would cause restlessness and sedation 24 hours a day, seven days a week. You can't sit and you can't have rest - it's very, very uncomfortable.

When I was first in hospital I had to accept this injection regime as part of the Magistrate's order. But when I was discharged from Hellingly or Oakwood, I was told I would still have to turn up for my injection at an outpatient appointment before being released into the community. But when I was released I wasn't prepared to accept the injections any more, so if I had a job or some cash at the time, I would just get in my car and go. I wouldn't turn up for any more injections and I would feel great, wonderful and like I was human again. But the paranoia would return and I would go onto develop even more serious delusions. I would usually end up living rough and be readmitted - I don't know if the nurses took bets on when - then they would try the same treatment. During my last admission to Oakwood in 1991, I managed to negotiate with them that I would be put on tablets – chlorpromazine (Largactil) and trifluoperazine (Stelazine). I knew other patients were receiving tablets and had threatened to put a brick through the window if they gave me any more injections. I've hardly missed a day of medication since then.

I would have accepted the life at places like Hellingly and Oakwood, living in a ten-bed all male dormitory with no privacy, maybe being sent to industrial therapy to pack soap or assemble valves for £1.70 a week. But it was the hell of the injections that always made me get myself discharged. I would be a model patient and be discharged to some situation in the community such as a local authority or Richmond Fellowship hostel. Once when I was discharged in Putney in about 1985 I managed to get a job in the City of London for four years as an accounts clerk and bought a house near Woolwich. When I bought my house I was able to avoid having injections, unlike when I was in the hostels where there was supervision for the injections. I became deluded and paranoid again and was made redundant and my house was repossessed. If I'd been able to get another job and keep the house, where I'd be now I don't know. At that time I survived for about five years without a home and it's taken me a long time to get back from that period of homelessness. I got

£13,000 from the proceeds of the sale of my repossessed house but was unable to get myself out of bus shelters. I stopped signing on the dole and put the money into a Post Office savings account, taking £50 a day out and just travelled round the South East. By that time I was quite severely deluded and thought the Russians must be coming, that rain was being sent over me from the Chernobyl disaster, and that the IRA was lurking around country lanes trying to creep up on the Archbishop of Canterbury who they wanted to harm. I had this constant delusion that traffic was being sent round to follow me and became obsessed with helicopters.

I was living homeless around Maidstone and occasionally used to break into the occupational therapy hut at Oakwood and make myself a cup of tea in the middle of the night. Once I did that and the place was full of police, who arrested me and took me to the police station where I was Sectioned. This resulted in me being sent back to Oakwood - which was my last admission to an asylum. Here I was put on the correct medication which made me quite sedated but I was able to get up in the morning and do normal things. Ten years ago a psychiatrist at my community mental health team changed me from chlorpromazine (Largactil) and trifluoperazine (Stelazine) to olanzapine, one of the new atypical drugs, which had even less sedative side effects. In 1991, on release from hospital I was resettled to Bexhill, near Hastings in Sussex. Since then I haven't been an inpatient and have been treated in the community.

About six years ago I needed a bit of extra support due to experiencing some difficulties with anti-social behaviour from my neighbours. This was provided at a crisis house called the Sanctuary and I spent about 18 months in supported accommodation for people with mental health problems, until they found me my present flat in social housing. I am sure if Hellingly and Oakwood had still been open I would have been admitted, but I didn't need hospitalisation and was just given some extra support. I am grateful for this and I've lived a reasonable life since then.

Contact with mental health professionals

Looking back at my first admission to Hellingly I had certain issues which could have been dealt with. They could have applied for an aegrotat degree for me, when you get an honorary award of a pass if you are ill at the time you take your finals. They could have given me help to recover the sum of money which I'd put into the family firm. Also I'd stopped being involved in the drug underworld at that time for a number of years and would have been happy to tell the police all I knew about the drug scene in Reading. Those three things could have been done to give me more confidence. But they weren't and I felt like a real low life. So I wasn't able to recover any of the status or hope which I'd lost or get some sort of future.

In my 'revolving door' days I don't think mental health professionals helped me very much. The consultant psychiatrist who was treating me in the asylum didn't recognise the tremendous discomfort I was in after being given the injections. I'd just be told on the ward round they were going to increase the medication. This changed vastly when I left the asylums and started being treated in the community. The people at the local day centre that I've attended regularly over the past 20 years have been very helpful, particularly the manager who encouraged me to finish my degree. One of her colleagues, a local mental health manager, was also very friendly and amenable. I have found that a lot of people in social care over the past few years have been approachable and will talk to you. This is a massive improvement on the days of the asylum. When they prescribed injections for me at Hellingly in 1975, this nurse with a Teddy boy hairstyle and a white coat would come up to me with a hypodermic syringe in a tray and say, "You can have your injection the hard way or the easy way". But nowadays you can talk to mental heath professionals and they have no limits to what they think you can achieve.

Transition towards recovery

Strangely enough, the person I have got to thank for things starting to improve for me was Margaret Thatcher. She's not always associated with social justice and I'm not what you'd call a typical Thatcherite. But I've got her to thank for closing the asylums down with a piece of legislation called the 1990 NHS and Community Care Act. After this was introduced I was discharged from the asylums into the community and I haven't been readmitted since. I haven't reoffended which has caused me less hassle, caused my carers and family less stress, and I've managed to get a BA degree in Politics with the Open University and a MA degree in Social Policy from Brighton University. My MA has helped by giving me some common currency with people in the mental health world and an understanding of the issues like social exclusion, early intervention and recommissioning.

In the days of John Major's Government, service users began to be involved in the planning and delivery of care. This is one of the phrases in the 1990 community care legislation, so we had things like user groups, a user charter and user democracy. This was the start of empowerment for me. People like the then-Health Secretary Stephen Dorrell started to talk about social exclusion as a concept in British social policy around the mid 1990s and Tony Blair established a social exclusion unit at the Cabinet Office. I think I benefited from this political change. I've also got to thank Gordon Brown for keeping inflation low for ten years when he was Chancellor. Inflation was going up all the time in the 1970s and people on a low income are always hit hardest by this. If you hadn't got a house that was doubling in value every two years you got left behind.

Another thing that happened with the liberation of community care was that advocates and self advocates like Survivors Speak Out and Survivors' Poetry started up. One of the main things they encouraged which I have found to be very helpful was the writing down or painting or setting to poetry or music of narrative. Narrative has been one of the most cathartic tools I've had around my relationship to my difficult past and encouraging others to do a narrative is a very therapeutic thing to do. Mental health professionals can better understand the people they care for by getting them to do a narrative of things that have been troublesome to them. It's pretty helpful to get those things down and I have given mine a lot of times. I've written about some of my experiences when I was most deluded which have been put into a book called *The Durham Light and Other Stories* published by Chipmunka Publishing. I also do PowerPoint slide shows and cartoons of my history in the mental health world which all reside on a free to use website called Slideshare *www.andrewsasylumlife.co.uk*. I've been encouraged to do those at the day centre and it's so useful. People will read it and think, yes, I wasn't alone in thinking those delusions too. I'd recommend that anyone with psychosis does a narrative of their life or things that have troubled them in the psychiatric system, write a song, do a poem or write it down. If people want to see what can be done with narrative, get in touch with National Perceptions Forum or Rethink which has a wonderful magazine and website full of people's stories around mental health.

Making recovery a reality

I've never really had a moment when I've thought, "Great, recovery is about to happen". But I know it's one of the policies of the local mental health Trust and I do approve of it, especially where people can take control of a bit of their lives, get some hope and insight. It's sort of a journey and is just about small steps. Personally I would count becoming a member of the property-owning democracy as real recovery but I haven't known people who have done that unfortunately.

Lots of things that are going on in my life have helped in my recovery. I like doing my slide shows and showing them at various events like mental health days or first aid training days. We're making some music and having a concert, and I've helped write some songs for that which is a bit of a laugh. Last year we wrote a song called *Time to Change* for the mental health campaign of the same name which we played in Hastings and is now on YouTube. I'm hoping to start a social enterprise this year which aims to deliver creativity with music, art and theatre workshops. Taking my BA and MA helped me. I also go to the gym most days which is good for my wellbeing, particularly as I take olanzapine which can make you put on weight. So recovery is about participating in society, keeping busy and doing something useful. It's about being comfortable with your life and doing things which are therapeutic and creative.

Hope

Some of the things I hope for are so big and unobtainable I know that I've got a very small chance of them happening. I'd like to get a place with my girlfriend, ideally where we could both have our own space in the house, but unfortunately it's unrealistic so I don't bring myself to hope for that.

The future gives me hope. One great hope is that I can register this social enterprise so we could do the kind of projects that I know of in London, such as Core Arts in Hackney where they have got their own really independent creative, service-user orientated centre, here in Sussex. It would be great to do a couple of concerts this summer. Hopelessness was being a revolving door patient where there's no future on the wards, or living in your car or sleeping in woods or bus shelters. I hope my story will have a positive impact on a number of individuals, especially if they have some creative inclination.

Reflection

I am very heartened that when I've been identified as someone with mental health problems, people haven't come up to me in the street and said, "I always knew you were a nutter". I think that is a mark of what you can expect nowadays - you won't get abuse though there are glass ceilings and things that can hold people back. In my experience I've been able to be honest with people about my mental health problems and it's not had a bad effect on me. But I would rather have not had psychosis, would have liked to have been able to fulfil my potential and have a decent relationship and children when I was younger. That would have been a much better outcome than spending my life in and out of mental institutions and being supported by a day centre for 20 years. There are lots of good things around living in communities and supported accommodation, like solidarity, but a normal life is probably a lot better. Mental illness has given me a focus though, for writing my slide shows and doing music.

Conclusion

To someone being treated with psychosis for the first time, I would give this advice. Speak up for yourself, get information on what the treatment means, on the side effects and benefits of having treatment. Don't just accept the first thing that is told to you and find out what works for you. Get talking therapies if you need them and if you can, maybe start to express your difficulties in various ways because others might like to know about them. Get help, get an advocate and some idea of what self advocacy is available and don't just accept everything that is given to you.

Recovery's Shooting Star

Photo: Jane Fradgley

Chapter 6

Recovery's Shooting Star

Michelle McNary, 35, from Clapham, South London, is a film maker who experienced ten years of untreated psychosis before being hospitalised and diagnosed with schizoaffective disorder. She has now been in recovery for over a decade and recently completed her first documentary on recovery from a service user perspective.

Background

I left school and did some horrible office jobs for years on end. But I wasn't any good at them, getting sacked from some and leaving others. At the time my brother was doing A levels in Media and Film Technology and suggested that we put our money together to buy ourselves a camera. So I agreed and really got into doing stills photography. I loved the freedom of going out and taking photos and still get a real buzz from it today. Since I was a kid I'd had a passion for film - I think it's an excellent way of communicating a message. You can be quite political, even with documentaries, and people don't realise. My dad was really into acting and films, often bringing home movies for us to watch. He had lots of film books and I remember wanting to read them and find out more. So when my brother encouraged me to go back to college and get some qualifications, I decided to study film. After getting four good GCSEs, I did a London Open College Network foundation degree in Film with A level Film Theory. It was brilliant because it combined both stills photography and video work. After this I went to Bournemouth Film School for two years to do a Higher National Diploma in TV Production and learned how to be a director. During my time at film school I wrote my first short drama called *Virago* which was shot on 16mm film. I started getting extremely ill while I was there. I was always teetering on being agoraphobic and having anxiety but could deal with it to a degree. I got really bad symptoms of paranoia and delusions, and wasn't eating properly or taking care of myself. It was surprising and quite an achievement that I actually managed to make a film in my second year as I was so ill.

Transition towards illness

Back in London I didn't feel quite so bad and thought the symptoms would pass. I was living in South London with my boyfriend and had a series of jobs in the film industry. I worked as a production assistant at a new media company, as a production manager for the National Film School and as a runner in Soho. But I didn't really find what I wanted to do and spent quite a lot of time unemployed. In 2000, I started to get sick again when I wasn't getting anywhere in making films. The onset was very slow and I would hide it, but it got progressively worse. When I was ill, I could never seem to get a film up and running. Things would happen, I'd take jobs that didn't work out or other people wouldn't appreciate my behaviour. The thought that I was destined never to make a film again made me feel really unhappy.

The illness, mixed with my sense of failure, started to take hold of me. The paranoia and delusional thoughts were intensifying. I was staying in a horrible dingy flat in Gipsy Hill which wasn't conducive to a healthy environment, but didn't leave because I thought I was going to be stabbed if I went outside. Day after day, whenever I went into the kitchen I would hear a maniacal laugh. I thought it must be workmen and went outside to check what was going on. In my head I envisaged they were building a gibbet and were waiting to hang me. My response was to take off all my clothes, stand on the table in front of the window, throw my arms out and shout, "Here you fuckers, now you can see me!" The laughter stopped and never came back, so I thought to myself that it couldn't be a coincidence. They could see me but I couldn't see them. The fact that the laughing stopped almost proved that I wasn't mentally ill. I was trying to kid myself and didn't want to admit that I was getting sicker and sicker. It wasn't just my mind that was going, but my physical state too. I wasn't eating properly and lost a huge amount of weight, dropping down to about seven stone. I was drinking heavily to self-medicate but also detoxing my diet, so was getting really bad stomach aches. I was doing too much exercise, getting up at 6.45am every morning to do yoga then going to the gym for two hours or more. I thought I was failing and that the only way I could control my life was through my eating and my environment. If I could control that, then it meant that I wasn't mentally ill.

Realisation of problem

Things eventually came to a head one day. I told my boyfriend I was scared of being stabbed when I went outside the flat, which made him think something was wrong with me. I was completely delusional and couldn't even speak properly. Suddenly I had this overwhelming feeling that someone was going to come and lock me up in a psychiatric hospital. I told my boyfriend this then a short time later, looked out of the window of my flat and saw an ambulance. So I panicked and hid in my bedroom, shouting, "They're coming to get me!" I didn't realise that my brother's fiancée had already called an ambulance for me. But before the psychiatrist arrived I calmed myself down and managed to hide what was going on. Someone from the local mental health team assessed me and said I was OK, but to call them out again later if needed. But I continued to deteriorate and a week later, my boyfriend took me to A&E at King's College Hospital. I was talking a load of old gibberish by this point about how we were going to leave the Earth and go to Mars. When we eventually saw a psychiatrist after waiting for 11 hours, I told him about this plan. Finally, I was Sectioned and was initially sent to Cygnet Hospital in Beckton as there weren't any beds at King's. The following night I was taken to Lambeth Hospital where I was to spend the next six months on a psychosis ward.

Once in hospital I kept pleading to be let outside, but the doctor was very strict and wouldn't even let me go down to the shops with a nurse. I felt like one of those animals you see in terrible zoos that sway from left to right because they are stuck inside. It seemed like being in hospital was making me sicker. I was over-medicated on all sorts of drugs. The risperidone and quetiapine they kept giving me had terrible side effects like making me dribble. I had blurred vision and would pace up and down all day. I couldn't sit down and wasn't eating properly. I couldn't sleep but if I got rowdy or caused trouble they would give me lorazepam and I would drop off for a few hours. Being kept in hospital seemed like a complete abuse of my human rights and I was literally pulling my hair out.

Crisis points

There were all sorts of problems on the ward. I had some jewellery with me and one night decided to hide it under my pillow. The next day it was gone so someone had obviously come into my room and stolen my stuff. Even now when I close my eyes, I think when I open them again a face will appear in front of me. The male nurses would come into the female area of the ward, which I now know is not allowed. If you had your door shut they would put the light on every hour to check you were in there. So I had really bad sleep deprivation to add to all the other problems because this light would keep waking me up. Nobody told me I could just leave my door open so they could stick their heads in and have a look.

Just the thought of going into a mental hospital had scared me but I eventually accepted that I needed hospitalisation. I'd suffered ten years of symptoms without treatment and I couldn't look after myself. I was a danger to myself and others, which is the reason why people get Sectioned. But I feel they could have handled my case a lot sooner, not let things drag on so long and not given me so much medication.

Contact with services and treatment

Being in hospital was driving me nuts - I felt like a caged bird. I was getting so desperate I started to self harm and even burnt my arm with a cigarette. The doctors offered me electroconvulsive therapy (ECT) which my family wasn't too happy about. But the doctors said I had quite bad depression and that it could help. With ECT, they attach electrodes to your head and it induces a fit. You're only in there for a few minutes and it makes you feel a bit groggy. I had about six or eight sessions and was laughing when I came out. It must have worked, because I started to feel better and about a week later, was put on clozapine. Before that they had tried three or four other drugs and nothing had worked. But this was effective in getting rid of the horrible delusions and hallucinations and I've been taking it successfully for nine years now. I hadn't been given a date to be discharged from hospital and my consultant had told me I might have to go onto another long-term ward. So I planned to go to a Tribunal to get them to release me. But a lawyer contacted me first, wrote to the powers that be and they let me go about two weeks later. For about a year, I lived in horrible temporary accommodation while waiting for a council flat to come up. Eventually I got my own place in Clapham and have lived there ever since. I have never been readmitted to hospital and have been in recovery for over a decade now.

At the age of 31 I was diagnosed with schizoaffective disorder with catatonia. Schizoaffective disorder is schizophrenia with a mood disorder, so I have all the symptoms like paranoia and hallucinations but also have a problem with mood swings. I can get very anxious, panicky and very low. They were spot on with the diagnosis and I was kind of relieved. At least I knew what I had and it explained quite a lot. Before I was diagnosed it was awful. I didn't understand why I felt the way I did and certainly didn't think it had anything to do with a mental health issue. I just thought that it was to do with my relationship with my parents and bad things that had happened in my earlier life.

When I first left hospital, I thought I'd get over my illness, come off the meds and be back to a normal life. But I'm still taking clozapine and quetiapine and don't think I could drop them. Some people try to come off medication but I totally, religiously take mine every day. If I don't, I have a sense of feeling different and don't want to put myself through that. There are side effects to the medication including weight gain - I'm 11 stone and have never been able to get back to my previous weight of nine stone. Clozapine also makes you dribble at night, but I hope to take some anti-side effect medication to stop that.

Contact with mental health professionals

Mental health professionals have done their best to help me with limited resources. A good mental health professional is caring, dedicated and wants to make a difference. If they are there to support you, recovery is inevitable. The problem I find with some mental health professionals is that they don't listen. They make their own assessments and don't seem to connect with you. That can be very difficult for someone who is mentally ill because it's hard to express yourself and get them to understand. My clinical psychologist is a good listener - I've been meeting him for therapy and attending his recovery workshops for a few years now. He will say his bit then listen to what I've got to say, so it's a team effort.

I'm having cognitive analytic therapy with a brilliant therapist at St Thomas' Hospital which has been really helpful. We've looked into my past and how patterns form in my relationships. I told him this time last year I ended two really bad relationships, which left a bit of a scar. But the therapist listened and because of that, I started to trust him. The therapy works because it's a partnership and I know he's there for me. A few years ago, I had some therapy with a trainee clinical psychologist which wasn't very helpful. Trainee psychologists are sometimes very young, although a couple of them would have made good psychologists in the long term.

My period in hospital could have been made less traumatic. They could have let me out earlier and provided better aftercare. When you leave hospital and are put into a horrible dingy room with no one there to help, you can start getting depressed. They should put you on a housing list before you come out and make sure you go straight into a happy, stable home environment of your own. You need somewhere comfortable to call your own. People would probably have less relapses if they were put straight into this kind of environment. The housing situation and being on benefits were stresses I didn't need when I left hospital, though a social worker tried to help. You plummet from these responsibilities and it's hard to keep well under that kind of pressure.

Transition towards recovery

After I came out of hospital, I was really lost for a couple of years. I was going through the motions and had no direction. It took over a year to get my flat and until then I couldn't really get involved in anything. As soon as I got a place to live, my recovery started. Having that safe haven made a really big difference to my mental health because it's really affected by stress. I thought about what I was going to do and decided I needed to update my skills, because when I was at film school we didn't have the digital technology there is now. So in 2003 I enrolled for a Master's degree in Film and TV Production. As part of the course, I wrote the script and edited a film called *Big Exit* that was shown at two online film festivals and my actress got a special mention so I was really pleased. I'm doing an acting class which is hard work because I have to reveal myself after having been shut away as an editor for quite a long time. This class has brought me out of myself and has been a really positive thing to do.

Making recovery a reality

Listening to other people talk about their recovery has made me think about my own. In April 2010 I finished my first documentary which was produced in conjunction with the South London and Maudsley NHS Foundation Trust (SLAM) on the subject of recovery. It features four service users talking about their recovery from mental illness and is now up on the SLAM website. When I started working on the project two years ago I wasn't as well as I thought but now the film is finished, I am the most well I've been in nine years. Working on the project gave me something to strive for, a purpose, and has kept me alive and fresh. It also made me less introspective. When you're mentally ill, you can look at yourself too much but the project was a good way to come out of that. Recovery is hard work and you have to push yourself. There were a few stressful moments with the film, such as technical hitches and I felt under pressure at times, but I handled it very well and achieved a great end result. Every time I finish something such as the film, I feel prouder of myself and have a bit more self worth than before. Listening to the stories of the service users I interviewed for the film gave me a great sense of hope.

Therapy has also helped me a lot. When you're in recovery you can sometimes wonder where the mental illness started and having therapy can help you find out. We talk about certain situations that I would never have thought about. Sometimes I feel really awful leaving the sessions and wonder if I actually want to put myself through it. But even though it's sometimes really difficult, I'm glad to be dealing with some issues I've never dealt with before.

I didn't think recovery was possible until I started having therapy with my psychologist and attending his workshops. As one SLAM service user says in my film, the concept is quite new in the UK although it's been around in the United States for a long time. SLAM is really now focusing on recovery and I think that's marvellous. When I first came out of hospital I had no idea there was a recovery movement but I've become aware of it through the writings of psychologists Patricia Deegan, Peter Chadwick and Julie Leibrich.

I particularly love Patricia Deegan, who is so insightful, on the ball, intelligent and inspiring. Once I'd read about her own experiences of recovering from mental illness I had someone to look up to, a role model. I thought, "If this girl can do it I'm going to give it a try!" I'm now proud to be a part of this movement through my work on the film and book.

I've achieved a lot in my recovery - I haven't relapsed in nine years and am leading a meaningful life. I have a purpose and am trying to get out there to do classes, socialise and make friends. Although I am making headway in my recovery, I'm not completely there yet. People just think I am well all the time because I don't talk about it, but I'm not. There still are difficult moments, like the other day I was meant to go shopping but couldn't because I felt very agoraphobic. But I just think it will pass and move on. I don't think it's possible to recover totally unless you suddenly stop taking all your medication and have got no symptoms, which isn't going to happen for most people. You are always in recovery because there is so much more you can be doing to help yourself. But the more I learn about my illness, the more recovered I get.

Hope

Hope has been very important in my recovery. You have something to strive for if you are hopeful and positive about your recovery. I was hopeless for those ten years when I was struggling with my untreated illness, but I began having hope when I first started reading the work of Patricia Deegan and having therapy sessions. There's a bit in my film called *Recovery: New Beginning, New Hope* and when people see it, the message that hope is important will get out there. I hope people will watch my film and think about where recovery comes from.

The next film I hope to produce is called *Climbing Walls*, about a young woman who is suffering from psychosis and how her family respond. The reason the film is called *Climbing Walls* is because that's how I felt in hospital. The film could be shown in schools or on mental health websites to help young people learn more about mental illness. There are probably a lot of young people fighting these symptoms without actually understanding them. I just want people to understand how terrifying it is to be mentally ill and go through a psychotic episode. Having hallucinations and not being in control of yourself is scary. I also want the film to illustrate how vulnerable you are in the mental health system.

Hope is linked to the future and in years to come, I would like to have my own house, a partner and be doing what I love, which is directing films.

I've got a burning desire to do my art but have to be careful with stress, as directing can be very challenging. I see myself enjoying life and getting more recovered but I'd like to be a lot more confident and not so self-conscious. I also have an idea about setting up a film club for people with mental illness so they can watch, talk about and make films.

Reflection

The interesting thing about being mentally ill is that you can sometimes see it in other people before they can see it in themselves. They are trying to function in the real world but you want to shake them and say they need help. I wish someone had said that to me - if enough people had then I would have done something about it a lot earlier. A person who is ill with psychosis for the first time can do several simple things to help themselves. Take your meds, get enough sleep, eat properly, go to the gym, force yourself to do things and don't sit indoors alone. Take the help when it's offered to you. The people in my film all talk about what has helped them in their recovery, whether it's family relationships, therapy, talking about their past or the things they enjoy like art or poetry. Don't dismiss any of these things. If you can take small steps and don't be too hard on yourself then you have a good chance of recovering yourself.

Conclusion

Before I got sick, I was never really myself and it can sometimes feel like the psychosis happened to somebody else. But now I'm in recovery, I'm finding out who I really am. In the film, we talk about recovery feeling like a kind of rebirth, which some people might think is a bit melodramatic. But it's true and I feel like I've been given a second chance. I'm finding out more about myself and have got lots to look forward to in the process.

From a Scribble To a Straight Line

Photo: Jane Fradgley

Chapter 7

From a Scribble To a Straight Line

Ben Haydon, 39, from Lewisham, South East London, is an artist who developed psychosis in his early twenties and has had 15 years of psychiatric treatment. He is now in recovery and successfully exhibits and sells his art work, recently holding a solo show at the Bethlem Gallery.

Background

At the age of 19, I was at Southwark Art College studying for a diploma in Fine Art. I was your average art student, doing drugs and graffiti, going to raves, and trying to be a DJ. I had the same teenage insecurities, self doubts and attitudes to life as everyone else. But art college wasn't teaching me enough and I was bored of looking at paintings in books, so I dropped out. I had a strong desire to get away from everyone and England, so I decided to put on my backpack and travel around the world. For a while, I did washing up jobs to try and earn enough money to go away. I was a very keen on photography and the idea was to become a freelance globetrotting documentary photographer and sell my work to National Geographic or Reuters. While I was travelling I was going to try and build up a portfolio to get my career started. So at the age of 21, I headed off on my own to experience the world and grow as an artist. From London, I went to Bali first then travelled all around Indonesia, Thailand, Malaysia and Singapore.

Transition towards illness

My mental illness was slowly building up inside me over the years and now was the time for it to explode. Around four months into travelling, I was in Thailand having a great time when my illness hit me. Suddenly one day everything was different. I went from being happy to having extreme paranoia and hallucinations, disorientation and panic. I found myself hiding in a guest house in the north of Thailand, thinking people were talking about me or watching me on camera all the time. I spent a lot of time getting deeper and deeper within myself and more complex paranoia. It felt like there were bugs and conspiracy theories all around me and I thought the Triads were following me. For a few days I travelled around the little villages of northern Thailand, thinking if I could escape from there to another place I would be safe. Then I managed to get a plane to Hong Kong, believing if I could get out of Thailand I'd be alright. But of course I wasn't and when I got to Hong Kong everything was still confusing. Everyone was still talking about me and making me ill and paranoid on purpose.

I spent a few days in a hotel room hiding under the duvet reading my *Lonely Planet* guide book and trying to work out where to go. I was convinced that cameras were watching everything I was doing and I needed to get home. Somehow I managed to catch a flight back to London but when I arrived at Heathrow, I still felt the same. Early in the morning, I got to my parents house and just stood there panicking in floods of tears. They realised something was seriously wrong and my mother called the doctor straight away. By the end of the day I was admitted to Bexley Hospital for what was initially hoped to be a one-off psychotic experience.

Realisation of problem

But unfortunately it wasn't and so began 15 years of psychiatric treatment. I spent three months in hospital getting back to a kind of sense of reality and was diagnosed with schizophrenia in 1991. I was in and out of Bexley Hospital on a regular basis until 2001. At the beginning I didn't believe I was ill – it's hard to believe that when you don't know what to believe or who to trust anyway. It just seemed like deep down everyone was plotting to cause me harm. Whoever I turned to, everyone was trying to do something spiteful or evil to me in some kind of way. I didn't even trust my parents. But once I'd been in hospital a few times, I accepted that I had an illness and didn't fight it. Even if I didn't trust the psychiatrist, I wasn't too proud to accept any help that was given to me. There was something inside me that would say, "Just go with it and see what happens". There was nothing else I could do anyway because I felt so trapped.

Crisis points

When I first got ill I was panicky, insecure, paranoid and depressed. A big thing from the start was feeling that everyone hated me and was trying to put me down. I was hypersensitive to how other people acted towards me and could be very hurt by little things people might say in conversation. About six or seven years into my illness, I got more assertive, high and aggressive. For many years I was reasonably stable but had a growing drink problem, thinking I might as well drink because I was as well as I was ever going to get. I was in a rut, thinking I couldn't do anything apart from sit in pubs or walk around the streets drinking beer. As I'm quite a vulnerable person, I would get involved in fights which would panic me afterwards and make my illness worse.

Over the years, the doctors tried me on many different drugs but they had lots of side effects and I couldn't get on with them. I was depressed and very anxious so was taking antidepressants as well as the antipsychotic drug risperidone. The side effects of rolling eyeballs, locked arms, muscle twitches and constant restlessness made me very stressed. After ten years of this medication I started wondering actually how ill I was and wanted to come off it. I felt so disabled by it and increasingly that I wasn't ill anyway. So I stopped taking it suddenly and didn't tell anyone.

Quite early on in my illness, I'd made the decision to live independently, first in a private rented flat and then in supported housing. I didn't want to be seen as someone who still had to live with his parents. In one flat I suffered abuse and theft of my belongings by people who took advantage of my vulnerability. I had to return to live with my parents until alternative accommodation could be found. This left me at a low point in my life and coincided with my coming off medication.

The illness started to build up again over a period of a month and got out of control. The voices took over, always telling me how useless I was and how I would be better off dead. For the first time in my life I was in danger of being Sectioned rather than going into hospital voluntarily. It was my fear of this that made me try a new medication. I ended up back in hospital where they put me on amisulpride and this has proved to be the most successful drug I've taken so far.

Contact with services and treatment

Amisulpride has been like a wonder drug for me. All the other drugs were keeping me well to a certain extent but not giving me the space or opportunity to improve. After three years of taking it, I'm more well than I've ever been in my entire life. The medication reduces the delusional thoughts and helps me keep the voices on a different channel. There are minimal side effects apart from very achy, tired legs so I can't walk far or run. But it's good that I've slowed down as I used to be a very restless person for many years.

I still have the voices - they won't go away - but over the years I've got stronger. They constantly banter and tell me things to wind me up. Sometimes I can be in a good mood with them but it still wears me out. The voices get confused and entwined with other people's conversations if I'm in the cinema, a pub or other crowded area. It's hard to distinguish if people are saying things to me. But with the medication I'm now on, I can prevent the voices taking control of me.

Medication has also calmed down the anxiety and paranoia, allowing me to think more clearly and putting me more in touch with reality. It means I am more able to concentrate and think ideas through. Before the medication I was consumed with the illness, and wasn't thinking like an artist or about painting. But now I can talk about things with people and it doesn't have to be just about the illness.

At the moment I meet up with a psychiatrist and psychiatric nurse twice a year for a review and to look at my care plan. The psychiatric nurse also comes to see me every couple of weeks, which is reassuring. It's important to know there is someone there in the background who is making sure things are ticking over as it helps me be stronger in myself and stay out of hospital. My last admission to hospital was in 2001. I'm happier now than I've ever been, though a lot more tired and slow after everything I've been through.

Contact with mental health professionals

As soon as I got back to a reasonable state of reality after one hospital admission, I was offered an occupational therapist. The help I've had from occupational therapists over the years has turned out to be some of the most important in my recovery. As an outpatient at Southbrook Road Community Mental Health Team in Lewisham, I would visit my occupational therapist every week and have a therapy session. She would get me involved in various projects and therapeutic activities, like going to drop-in centres. These are very important when you are mentally ill, because if you haven't got anything to do, you're lost. A picture framing course I took at the Ladywell Centre has given me a qualification so I can now frame my own and other people's paintings at a cheap price. My occupational therapist found me the opportunity to have a solo exhibition at the Bethlem Royal Hospital art gallery in Beckenham last November. She also helps me organise the practical bits of my life such as sorting out problems with debt. My last psychiatric nurse helped me exhibit at the Novus Gallery and being at the opening, inviting my guests and also selling some of my work was one of the proudest moments of my life.

An occupational therapist is very important to work with, because they can become like a friend. On a professional basis, they can help you to build confidence and open doors to activities for you to be involved in. Gaining their trust is a big help in terms of recovery. It was also a big bonus that the psychiatrist and occupational therapist worked with my parents, who would come to some of the meetings when I was an outpatient. Keeping in touch with my occupational therapist or psychiatric nurse has helped to give them a better understanding of how I was feeling.

When a patient has paranoia they are not going to believe what professionals like psychiatrists or occupational therapists tell them to begin with. It takes a while for the person to believe the illness and treatment are not all being done on purpose. But looking back on it all, I've been looked after very well in hospital and couldn't have asked for anything to have been done differently. I have got no complaints with the good psychiatric care I've had from the NHS over the years.

Transition towards recovery

My illness didn't really improve until I started taking the amisulpride. Before then I didn't think it was possible to recover. For ten years I would get to a reasonable level of wellness so I could be discharged from hospital, then my illness would wear me down again. There were periods of relative stability, when I felt my head was clear, could talk to people and do things. But I was still ill and always sank down after a short period of time. Now I'm taking amisulpride, I feel better than I've ever been before. I am also more experienced in how to deal with my illness.

Making changes to certain aspects of my lifestyle that were restricting me has been an important step in my recovery. They were keeping me in a juvenile rut for many years but now I am maturing as a person and artist. I used to listen to electronic dance music on Kiss FM but it got tiresome and monotonous. So I discarded it and now just listen to classical music on Classic FM all the time as company. My life is so much better now I've got rid of the television. I've cut down on my drinking and no longer walk around the streets with a can of beer. I spend time with family and like going to the cinema. Although many friends have disappeared over the years, there have been a few that have kept in contact, accepting me without being judgemental. So I'm building up my circle of friends from way back in my school days. Having my own place to live has been important for my self esteem and giving me the space to paint. My flat is like another canvas and I'm constantly doing it up, trying to make a nice home for myself.

I've been able to get back to doing my painting and thinking and working like an artist. My studio is set up at home and I work there every day. I've always got something to be working on, such as an exhibition and it takes two or three years to get a collection of canvases together. Hopefully I'll have another exhibition at the Bethlem Gallery in a few years time. Other projects pop up in between exhibitions. Last year one of my paintings was featured on the front cover of the *British Journal of Psychiatry*. The painting is about coping with the highs and lows of schizophrenia; and drinking on the streets and being stuck in a rut. I used a dog to represent the lows and a euphoric smiling devil as the highs in an abstract form in oils and spray paint, the two main media that I work in. The red lines around the edge of the painting symbolise the prison of the mind and a route to self destruction, with a black background as an expression of the dark side.

My art comes first and I don't want to share a living space with someone else. I had a relationship with a woman for five years but now I'm happy to be single. I'm very cautious about passing schizophrenia onto my children and as an artist feel I need to live on my own. Seven years ago, my parents got me a dog from Battersea to keep me company. Mimi is one of the best things that has ever happened to me. She's given me the opportunity to be responsible for someone other than myself, to take care of and accompany me to places where I might not be confident enough to go alone. Owning a dog has also been very therapeutic because it gets me out walking and she's also inspired me a lot over the years.

Since these changes have taken place, I've managed to turn my life around. Now I'm going in a straight line rather than a scribble.

Making recovery a reality

Recovery means being able to live with my voices and accept that they are coming from inside me, not outside. It means experiencing happiness after years of often feeling nothing or not knowing how to laugh or even smile properly. My recovery is not complete and I still find myself slipping, but the difference is now I can recognise it and ask for help. Recovery is about continuously getting stronger and improving my lifestyle, which is getting better all the time.

My art has been my therapy in my journey towards recovery along with the medication. I use art as a constructive coping strategy and work on my painting to keep occupied and well. The work I do is not just about mental illness. I'm more interested in exploring other things and I'm trying to learn about the world through my painting. My illness is an annoyance that I have to live with but I can set it aside when I'm working and not let it consume me. Some of it still comes through because the illness and being an artist is combined and entwined. But my painting is now more about trying to make aesthetic canvases and I see art as mostly a release of self expression. Through my work, I'm trying to develop my own avenues of being self-employed and independent. Ideally I would like to have my own market stall in Greenwich in five years time so I can sell my prints, paintings and photographs.

I'm lucky enough to have supportive parents and know not everyone has this. They have been through a hard time coping with me over the years and we get on much better now I'm much less reliant on them. They have been really helpful in my recovery by being there to back me up while still recognising I need my independence.

The recovery movement is very important. Getting people involved in their own recovery through projects can offer a lot of therapeutic benefits. Recently I took part in a film and book on recovery which were produced by another service user for the South London and Maudsley NHS Foundation Trust. I was very nervous about appearing in the film but now I think it wouldn't be a problem to do it again, so it's made me stronger and more confident.

Hope

I've always had hope and it's been a big part of my recovery. Before I started taking amisulpride hope was all I had because I thought that was as well as I was going to get. Hope made me think that I could crack on for another day and get better. But for the first few years of my illness, I lost hope because I was experiencing very deep depression and felt suicidal on a few occasions. I lost all hope that I would ever get better and just went along with struggling with the illness and medication.

My hope for the future is eventually to get a painting exhibited in the Tate Gallery or Tate Modern. It's not important whether this actually happens or not - what's important is aiming for that goal. I still hope to go off and see other countries. Last year I flew to Australia with my parents for my sister's wedding. Managing to socialise with so many new people was not something I could have dealt with a while ago but I felt good about it this time. There are paintings I want to go and see for real rather than just looking at them in books. I went to Belgium in April for a long weekend because I wanted to see the Magritte paintings in Brussels. This made me stronger and built up my confidence again that I could go off on my own abroad. So now I feel I could go anywhere in the world with my illness and it won't be too much of a problem.

I don't know if what I've said can give hope to anyone else, but it's good if it can. Now I don't feel I have a strong need for hope myself – I'm just getting on with my life and enjoying it.

Reflection

Psychosis has made me a stronger person although it's pretty much a nightmare when you're going through it all. The worst thing is feeling like you are a child and everyone else is somehow an adult. As you're not working, you have got that whole issue of being on benefits. For many years, I always felt younger than my age and only felt like I'm finally an adult in the last four or five years. Now I'm more independent and have come a long way, although it's taken a long time. I'm an artist and always have been, but I just happen to be mentally ill as well. Psychosis has given me ways of thinking about my art. I'm learning ways that my painting can strengthen me, keep me stable and stimulate my mind. It helps keep me positive about myself.

Based on my experience, I would give this advice to someone ill with psychosis. Try not to give up hope in yourself, take each day as it comes and don't fight the illness. Don't deny that you are ill and don't be too proud to ask for or accept help. Once you get rid of the paranoia, you can prevent the voices taking control too much, starting to even joke or be in a reasonable mood with them. You can find your way through which is a reason not to give up hope. Mental illness also improves with age and you get better at living with it – I remember being told that by an older artist with schizophrenia at an art therapy group I used to attend.

Conclusion

What is mental illness at the end of the day? It's something we all go through, but people experience it on different levels and intensities. Everyone's experience of mental illness is different. How things turn out for you all depends on what you've done with your life, your views and beliefs. It also depends on the situations, childhood and occurrences that an individual experiences and what they have done in their life. Mental illness is so hard to diagnose because everyone is unique. In some ways it's like having a baby. When you first get it, it's all a mess at the beginning but you grow with it and go through a lot of things together. I know that I still often struggle to cope but also feel that I am getting stronger. There will be bad times but everyone has to go through these. I am learning how to live with my illness and make my lifestyle as therapeutic as possible. I've managed to get a lot out of my system and work things out for myself. In the process I'm learning about the world and life, and things are slowly slotting into place.

Black, Proud and Beautiful

Photo: Jane Fradgley

Chapter 8

Black, Proud and Beautiful

Bose Dania, 36, from Newham, East London, was working as a dancer in Austria when she first had a psychotic episode. It wasn't until her eighth hospital admission that she was diagnosed with schizoaffective disorder. Bose credits work, a supportive family and a positive attitude as being key components in her recovery.

Background

Although I'm a Londoner I was born in Lagos, Nigeria, while my mum was on holiday visiting family there. My dad is a Muslim so has three wives and 14 children, but separated from my mum when I was six months old. I grew up in Manor Park but my dad paid for me to go to a private school in Middlesex at the age of seven. At this school I met my older sisters for the first time – we'd grown up in different homes so I didn't know them too well. Dad was quite wealthy so they had a privileged lifestyle. My time at this school was a lonely experience because they didn't make any effort to befriend me and I didn't have any friends. Dad's business went pear-shaped so I left after one term and went back to live with my mum. It was a very hard childhood. As the eldest daughter in an African family, I had to do a lot of household chores. Our flat was very overcrowded, with mum, step-dad and six children living in just two bedrooms, and it was difficult to find the space to do my homework. Although I was happy around my brothers and sisters, my dad had gone back to Nigeria and I had a lot of issues with him not being there. School was tough because I was dyslexic, although didn't know this at the time and just thought I was a bad speller. I only found out at the age of 32 when I took a Creative Writing course at college. So I left school with one GCSE in Drama and always struggled with the written aspect of my studies.

But it was in performance that I excelled. Since the age of six my dream was to become famous like Michael Jackson - he was my inspiration and I had posters of him everywhere. I went to Westminster Kingsway College to study Performing Arts but due to the dyslexia, didn't get the grades I needed in my written work. It felt like there was no one I could talk to about my feelings, so at college I started writing poetry as a way of getting them out. Here I published my first poetry book called *A Silent Cry* and started doing performances of my work. I sold a hundred copies of the book in one week at £1 each, reinvested the money into having more copies printed, then sold them for £3.50 each.

We didn't have a lot of money when I was growing up so I was determined to make something of myself. Work was also my only way out of the house. Although I loved writing, my dream was to perform so I went to Barking College to do a Business and Technology Education Council National Diploma in Performing Arts. My mum was dead against me becoming a performer – she wanted me to be a doctor or lawyer – so when I went out to drama lessons I used to tell her I was going to a sewing class. In the evenings, I worked as an usherette at the Theatre Royal in Stratford to make money to pay for college. I loved the buzz and it wasn't like working at all. I got to watch the shows and talk to the actors, soaking up knowledge about the business like a sponge. But studying and working was hard. When I came in from college I had to go to work, then do my homework until 2am in the morning. But I stuck it out and finished college at 19. I'd moved out of home and was living in a hostel in Forest Gate when I decided I wanted to put on my own show. For about a year, I saved money to produce a show called *Black, Proud and Beautiful* that I'd written, directed and choreographed myself. At the time I was working as a care assistant and after my shift I would audition school kids for a part, hold rehearsals or go leafleting to promote the show. When the day of the performance arrived I was surprised at the turnout – the house was nearly full. But despite all this, deep down I was quite shy.

Transition towards illness

I did lots of different jobs along the way, eventually getting a three month contract to appear in a production of *Porgy and Bess* in Austria. When I went over there at the age of 23 it was the best time of my life. There were 90 black actors in the production from all over the world and I got to work with dancers who had studied in Berlin or New York. I had never seen a country as beautiful as Austria and wanted to live there permanently. Every three months, I was travelling back and forth from Austria to London, but decided I was going to move to Bregenz. Luckily a company approached me and asked if I'd be interested in teaching dance – mainly contemporary, jazz, freestyle and African styles. Although I'd never taught adults before, I agreed and signed up for a ten week course with them. I wasn't earning enough money to get my own place and had to share with other people, including one man who would come home late at night drunk and throw up his kebab. So to earn some more money I approached a college to see if I could teach there.

I couldn't speak German, didn't have any money and didn't know if anyone would come to my classes. But they lent me a hall free for three months to build up the dance school and I started to teach a class there once a week. To begin with only one person would turn up, but I would trudge through knee-deep snow to go and teach them. A friend told me it would never work, but my stubbornness kicked in and I was determined it would. A television station had previously interviewed me about *Porgy and Bess,* so I called them about my dance school and also appeared in the newspapers. When I arrived to teach my class the following week expecting just three students, the place was packed. From then on the school just took off. I had classes five days a week and the local school and community centres asked me to come and teach for them too. At the weekends I was a 'freestylist' which means I would go and dance in clubs. When pop artists like Public Enemy or CC Rogers would come to town, I would dance for them. I got to meet loads of artists and we always had great parties afterwards, smoking marijuana and staying up all night. The best part about it was that I'd never made so much money!

Realisation of problem

My life consisted of a lot of hard work and partying. The dance school was more successful than I could ever have expected, but Sunday was the only day I had to rest. I started to get ill but didn't know it. As I'd been interviewed in the media, people knew me but I didn't know them and this made me paranoid. The language barrier also made me paranoid as everyone was speaking in German when I was out in a group. I was asked to perform at an AIDS charity event so choreographed a dance to a Michael and Janet Jackson song, but on the day my dance was terrible and I didn't know what I was doing. The whole routine went out of my head and I ended up doing this manic, crazy dance. I also started to develop paranoia, hear voices and see images. So there was a sense that something was wrong, but I didn't know what it was. I just thought I could fight it if I kept on working.

Crisis points

Eventually, I couldn't take any more and decided I wanted to go home to London, so packed my bags and left. I stood in the street with the dance studio to my right and the train station to my left, and spent the whole day walking between them. The police must have noticed there was a problem, as they took me to the police station and called a doctor. It was late at night and they took me to hospital in an ambulance, which involved driving through the mountains. I believed it was the Second World War, they thought I was a spy and were taking me away to be gassed or killed. Inside the hospital, I thought they were taking me to a torture chamber for interrogation and that the injection they gave me was a truth drug. This injection knocked me out for a few days and I didn't know what was going on when I woke up. They gave me this medication that made my lips heavy and affected my speech. When I started to feel better, I tried to fool the doctors that I was OK. In Austria, your family has to take responsibility for you before you can come out of a psychiatric hospital or they won't let you into the community. So I called my family in London and said, "I'm in hospital and they're trying to say I'm mad." The joke has always been that I'm a bit crazy because I was always the party girl. After spending three weeks in hospital, my brother and sister flew over to get me and brought me back to London where my mum took me to see the family doctor.

At the time, it hadn't dawned on me that I had a mental illness. I just thought I'd got too big too fast and the Austrians were trying to destroy me. I thought because I was Black British and had been successful there was a conspiracy to try and get rid of me. I wanted to get back to my dance school and had a contract for a show starting in the summer, so after two weeks staying with my mum headed back to Austria. After dance class one day I went back to my flat and that's when it hit me that I couldn't do it anymore - I just wanted to come home. So I gave everyone their money back, closed down the school and returned to London in May 2000, three years after I'd first come to Austria.

Contact with services and treatment

Back in London I stayed at my mum's place, but needed to get out because being there brought back too many memories and was driving me crazy. So I moved into a bed and breakfast while I tried to get my own place. Work has always been my way of getting through everything, so I volunteered for a women's health project to keep occupied. Then I had my first psychotic episode in this country, which was a terrible experience. I was still smoking weed and would just sit in my room smoking and watching television all day. Lying on my bed one day, I had flashes of the paranoia I'd experienced in Austria. I began to think there was a bomb in the room and if I got off the bed, it would explode. I lay there for three or four days without eating or sleeping, but eventually had to warn others. So I got up and started going into other people's rooms to tell them there was a bomb about to go off. The hostel called an ambulance which took me to hospital and I was also seen by the police because I'd said my family was dead. I was then taken to a psychiatric hospital in Newham. Over the next three years, I was hospitalised seven times for psychotic episodes.

When I first came out of hospital I didn't want to eat or take a bath. I was like a baby and had to learn how to do everything for myself again. As I hadn't lived in London for a long time, I'd lost contact with friends and was very isolated. All I had was my family. So I started to do a college course to get me into the routine of having a shower, getting dressed and going out. I was on olanzapine but it made me very drowsy, so it was difficult to get up in the morning and I was always late for college. I'd begun to do voluntary work with the mental health charity Mind and got more information on mental health, finding out that I had rights and didn't have to take the medication I was given. So I told the doctor it wasn't working for me and stopped taking it. Whenever I did this, I'd become very withdrawn, have hallucinations, hear voices and my speech wouldn't make any sense. I would just smoke more weed to shut it out, then relapse again and end up back in hospital. Now I take risperidone every night and it's helped me a lot. I don't feel drowsy and feel like I live a normal life. I stopped smoking weed at around this time, which I'd been doing since I was 16 and my partner said he couldn't believe the difference in me. After my fifth hospitalisation, I was diagnosed with bipolar affective disorder which was changed to schizoaffective disorder three years ago. I thought to myself it didn't make a difference what they titled me because it was my journey towards recovery that mattered. Since then, I haven't had an episode and have lived a normal life.

Contact with mental health professionals

Mental health professionals such as social workers and nurses have sometimes hindered rather than helped my recovery. When I first entered the mental health system, I didn't know how I wanted them to help me. But now they are more helpful because I've been through so much and know what I want. For example, I'd tell them I wanted to work, but they would say I should rest, so I had to sort things out for myself. Everything I've got involved in, such as voluntary work or short college courses, I have organised myself by looking on the Do-It.org volunteer website or through the Volunteer Network. I just got sick of going to the nurse or social worker and saying I needed to do something to help me get well but not getting anywhere.

People with mental illness want to rebuild their lives but don't know how. All they need is a little support and guidance. But you don't get that in hospital, they just leave you there on medication. Medication does help, but you can take it and still not get back into society. You need the staff to give you that introduction back into society because you are so low when you come out of hospital.

It took ages to find a diagnosis but a psychiatrist gave me one during my fifth admission to hospital. He told me I could leave hospital because I was a voluntary patient, but if I did, would never get better and would eventually be back in again. I was in there for about four weeks but could always call him and he would come and try to understand what was going on in my mind. Although he was a very busy man, he always gave me time when I needed it. This helped me deal with my illness and begin to recover.

Transition towards recovery

After I came back to London and had my first episode, I needed someone to help me unravel all the stuff that was going on in my head. The waiting list for counselling in my area was very long, so I sourced some free counselling through the Salvation Army but it didn't work for me. I was very delicate and by the time the counsellor had got me to open up, it was time to go home. It felt like I'd ripped my heart out and she didn't bandage me up. I was just told to sit in reception and have a cup of tea before I left. So I stopped going and started counselling myself, which helped me begin to improve. I would sit on my own pretending to be a counsellor, asking myself questions and answering them. These questions included what caused my illness and how could my childhood have affected it. Everything I needed to get out of my system, I wrote down on a piece of paper which I ripped up.

I also did voluntary work which helped me a lot because it got me out of the house and interacting with other people. Before this I used to get depressed because I was at home on my own a lot. One of the first volunteering jobs I did after leaving my mum's was in a charity shop in Lewisham. I went in and said I needed to volunteer, but they told me it would take a couple of weeks to organise. But the manageress could see I was desperate to do something, so let me start the next day. I worked five days a week for six months, sorting out the clothes, tagging items and serving on the tills. Eventually I needed something more challenging for my brain, so started volunteering with Mind on mental health campaigns. I got to learn more about mental health issues and attended a reception at the House of Commons about women with mental illness in prison. Through my involvement with Mind, I did a bit of volunteering with the Afiya Trust, an organisation which campaigns for equality in healthcare for black and ethnic minority people. I even taught dance to other mental health service users as a way to get them to come out of themselves. Through getting involved in these activities, I was able to engage more with society, build up my confidence and meet new friends. Eventually I met my partner and two years ago gave birth to my son.

Making recovery a reality

In comparison with some of the people I was in hospital with, I know I've recovered. I live a normal life and am not just hiding away in my room, I look after my son and he's well. I've got a good support system and can do everything as normal.

My family, partner and son have helped me recover the most. When I was in hospital, my sister looked after my son and used to put him on the phone to me. This would make me cry because I missed him so much, but would make me even more determined to get well. Knowing he was safe with my family meant I could focus on getting better. My partner would travel for two hours every day to see me in hospital and that gave me a reminder that I had a life outside. He has really helped my recovery by teaching me how to communicate in a more effective way. If something bad happened to me before, like someone pushed in front of me in a queue, I would just go home, smoke joints and get depressed. I had a lot of issues from my childhood that I hadn't dealt with and was trying to protect everybody by not saying anything. But I have now learned how to communicate my feelings and have peace because everything has been aired. My family has tried to encourage me. Once my brother set all the poetry books I have written out in front of me and made me reread them. My sister used to say to me, "Look at all the things you've achieved. How many people would have the guts to go and work in another country?"

Hope

Hope is the only recovery. Hope is that the next day is going to be better than today. When I first came back from Austria, I beat myself up with self pity and nearly lost hope. I'd never made so much money in my life but was now penniless. I'd worked since I was 14 and was back to living in a council flat. I was down to nothing and was even wearing my sister's hand-me-down clothes. I was so dark and low, I never thought I'd find a loving partner, have a child or have peace of mind. But the hope started coming when I realised there *is* life out there beyond mental illness. In 2003 I went to my sister's wedding in the Dominican Republic. It was the first proper holiday I'd had in years and I interacted with people who didn't know I had a mental illness. This made me think I still had my communication skills and gave me confidence. So I started saving my money and took some more holidays, even going to see my uncle in Australia.

My writing gives me hope. Before I had my son I wrote a series of poems called *Understanding the Journey* which expressed how I felt in hospital, about the doctors and when I started to emerge from darkness into the light.

The poems are about fighting for your dreams, for example my poem *Feeling* describes how a new me is emerging.

My hope for the future is that my son can have the best childhood and life I can give him. Some days being a parent can be difficult, but then I look at him sleeping and it gives me hope. I hope to earn some money and eventually live happily as a family with my partner in one house.

Reflection

From the beginning I'd always told myself I was going to fight this illness and it wouldn't beat me. While I've always been a fighter, I've been stronger in some areas than others. I was strong at go-getting but at times I've been so low I've wanted to die. Once I lay on my road at six o'clock in the morning and waited for the cars to run over my legs. No one understood I was ill and my family said there was nothing wrong with me. When the illness is in your head, people expect you to act normally. But I thought that people would know I wasn't well if I had a physical illness or a broken leg. I was determined to get better and would pray that God would help me. I've always thought to myself that I'm not going to let myself be labelled mentally ill. Yes I have a mental illness, but it doesn't mean I can't live like everyone else. When people see me, they don't judge me. I make new friends who don't know I'm mentally ill, so when I get to know them and tell them my story, they can't believe it.

Self pity is the worst diagnosis, even worse than mental illness itself. I believe if you go into something with a positive mentality, then you will see the opportunities come your way. Mental illness is for life and I've accepted that there is always a chance I will have another episode, no matter how well I get. Everyone's symptoms are different but you need to be able to recognise the early signs so you can do something about it. I have a list of early signs I am aware of, such as lack of sleep, losing my appetite and being withdrawn, and by being aware of them, I can get to the illness before I have to go to hospital. If you research your diagnosis, then you can compare how you are feeling with the symptoms and recognise the difference.

Conclusion

There are two roads you can take when you are first ill. You can either stay the same or get through it. To get through it, you just have to believe that you are not going to be ill forever. Every day that I haven't had an episode is a good day. I take it day to day and don't think too far ahead. I am stronger than I realise. Before I was ill I had more money but was lonely. Although I don't have the money now, I'm richer in other ways.

Feeling

Feel like I'm emerging,
From darkness.
From a time, when demons controlled my mind,
With their different shapes and images
I found myself praying for death
As my only release.

Feel like I'm emerging,
From a time, when hope was a word
That didn't exist and the future
Was only a day at a time.

Feel like I'm emerging,
From a shell, that stood.
Broken, into pieces unrecognizable
Of it's former being.

Feel like I'm emerging
Like a new born baby.
Learning how to walk, the walk of life.
Learning who I am to become, who I am to be.
Feel like I'm emerging
To a new dawn, a new awaking.

Feel like I'm emerging,
Like a child, growing with every day
With society as my guidance
I feel my inner strength.

Feel like I'm emerging
From a time, when darkness was my only friend.
I -feel - like -I'm -emerging.

Copyright Bose Dania

Finding Poetry in Psychosis

Chapter 9

Finding Poetry in Psychosis

James Bellamy, 37, of West Norwood, South East London, is a poet who developed psychosis at the age of 20. This led to 15 years of treatment involving cognitive therapies and mental health medication. He responded well and has been in recovery for several years now, successfully publishing poetry and prose in many books and magazines.

Background

Looking back, I can see that I had been getting ill for a while. At the age of 18 I started feeling shaky and listless, panicky and nervous. My head used to spin but I thought it was just tiredness. During my last three years at school I'd experienced several crises. I had developed an unrequited fascination with a female student but she didn't want to know me. I was expected to get three A levels and go to Oxford University but ended up with just one because I couldn't cope with studying. My main passion of poetry had begun to deteriorate from a powerful exposition of thought and feeling into confused images and gobbledegook. Each one of these setbacks filled me with extreme fury and I was convinced the world around me was evil and deserved contempt. The stresses intertwined and I started to retreat into my own head, becoming paranoid and delusional. I thought the neighbours were trying to communicate with me through the walls and that I'd developed special psychic powers. Towards the end of 1992, I was on the verge of schizophrenia before falling over the edge into full blown illness. I was in the kind of state where a descent into mental illness shouldn't have been unexpected but I wasn't prepared when it finally did happen.

Transition towards illness

By April 1993 I was completely gaga. I was sitting in the sun at school, when I looked up at the clouds and began to hear voices in my head. Visual hallucinations convinced me that I was under threat everywhere I looked. As the months went on, the illness got progressively worse. One morning in early

June, I woke up to see visions of the Maharishi in front of me, proclaiming, "This madness plays havoc with my ears." I could also hear my two pet lizards talking in the most infuriating, snakish way. I heard voices from the television screen telling me there had been an alien invasion of Great Britain and that everyone was going to suffer and die. Wherever I looked, I could see distorted visions of Godliness and spirituality. I heard the voices of Christ and Jonah and saw many visions of healing and prophecy. I told my dad I'd found God and as an atheist he was very upset. He thought I must have gone loony and called in the doctor. But I faked sane, which was a mistake because I lost 22 months of treatment as a result.

Realisation of problem

After two more months of delusions and confusion, I finally accepted that I was ill. But I still didn't confess to my family or a doctor. I became convinced that the illness would clear up over the course of time and I could rid myself of the symptoms in all sorts of bizarre ways. In order to cure myself I began drinking too much wine and eating poisonous leaves from the garden. My family repeatedly asked me about my mental state, but I kept quiet because I was afraid of being put in an asylum. My father and sister eventually contacted Social Services but it wasn't until the neighbours did the same thing that something happened. They had heard me screaming out, "Go away" and "Leave me alone" in the middle of the night and it was clear that this situation could not continue.

Crisis point

Something had to be done, and I was finally Sectioned at the age of 21 after nearly two years without treatment. When the psychiatrist and social worker arrived to take me away I was terrified and refused to cooperate. The fear that this day would come had haunted me for months, so I ran out of the house and managed to evade them. Two days later, they returned with two policemen and I remember being put in handcuffs, shut in a meat wagon and taken to the Maudsley Hospital. As I was carried away I was screaming, "What's going to happen to me?" and "What about my poetry?" One of the reasons I shied away from treatment for so long is because I was scared I'd be shut away forever. Far from being locked away for good, I was told early on I would only be in hospital for a matter of weeks. This helped reassure me and start to trust the Maudsley, which I still do to this day.

Contact with services and treatment

My family was relieved it was finally over and so was I. After a couple of nights in hospital, I chose to cooperate with all treatments because I felt secure in my mind for the first time in months. Despite this, I requested an appeal against the Section and took part in a Tribunal to decide whether I would be released early. This only proved that I definitely did need treatment. During the Tribunal, I said I was part of a "Charles Manson Poetry School" and that televisions spoke to me. Unsurprisingly, the Tribunal agreed to a continuation of the Section, so I accepted the decision and settled into my treatment. This involved a regime of chlorpromazine, haloperidol and injections of flupenthixol (Depixol) into my buttock. The flupenthixol (Depixol) injections worked really well at reducing the voices but the chlorpromazine and haloperidol had bad side effects including twitching, so they were dropped. After spending nine weeks in hospital, I was allowed to go home to my father. I still suffered occasional symptoms but was on the road to recovery. Once I was discharged, I was assigned a clinical psychologist and a doctor. The doctor diagnosed me as a chronic schizophrenic, which made me sad. I had hoped it wouldn't be schizophrenia and wanted to get back to being sane, but the prospect was very small. Post diagnosis, I tried to have a positive outlook. I've been living in the community since 1995 and this has been a very productive time for both me and my family.

When I first got out of hospital I used to sleep a lot because I was experiencing certain symptoms that were so bad it wasn't possible to do anything else. I could go without voices for days at a time which was wonderful but felt I had cat's eyes causing burning pain in the back of my head and had to lie down until they stopped. To deal with this, my psychiatrist put me on risperidone which was brilliant for two whole years. I recovered enough that the Mosaic Clubhouse, a resource centre for people with mental illness in Balham, referred me to a training placement. But that was a mistake and four months in I had a complete relapse which lasted for several years. I don't know what caused it but one day I woke up and was ill again. My mind was spinning with voices all the time, drugs weren't working and I had to do something about it. In 2005 I was admitted to hospital voluntarily for 18 nights so I could be put on a titration for clozapine, which I've been on for five years now. Being on the right medication at last has helped me a great deal and without it, I don't know where I would be. I'm too scared to try and come off the medication because I think the symptoms would come back straight away.

Over the past fours years there has been a vast improvement in my mental health. I have responded well to treatment and my state of mind is now relatively healthy and sane. I still have some symptoms, primarily hearing voices, but much fewer these days than years ago. The voices combine with visual hallucinations to abuse me, shouting and screaming that I'm worthless, stupid or a nobody. Sometimes they are vile, perverted sexual hallucinations about being raped or killed. On being discharged from hospital, I began to explore my symptoms with my psychologist. This helped me feel more at ease with my situation and my personality stabilised to something approaching normal. My psychologist made me understand that disembodied voices are not real or caused by other people. Now I am aware of them and comfortable with the fact that they are part of me, I have a sense of calm and inner peace which means that the illness has weakened.

Contact with mental health professionals

Over the years many doctors, psychiatrists, psychologists and psychiatric nurses have given me vital support and without their help I'd be dead. The way they have talked to me has helped me understand what's going on with my mental illness. They have given me a sense of self importance so I don't have to curl up in a ball and die. I've had all sorts of therapy including cognitive behavioural therapy which has helped me understand myself and developed my capacity to see through the illness.

Working with my psychologist has been extremely helpful in my recovery. His forthright behaviour and attempt to understand me has put the illness in perspective. I needed to listen to him and always understood the things he said to me. This has made me feel better and better. He informed me that recovery from mental illness was a possibility when I never thought it was before. When I was first treated, I was told that you're sort of dead when you're mentally ill. But the more I understand recovery is possible, the more I improve. Thanks to my psychologist, I now have insight into my illness and understand it more. He also got me involved in all sorts of recovery work, including 12 weeks of workshops where we discussed leading a meaningful life. Trying to see the meaning of life as not related to mental illness and speaking to the other people who attend the groups is very helpful. This psychologist encouraged me to take part in a film and book on recovery which were produced by another service user for the South London and Maudsley NHS Foundation Trust. This helped me to become more fully aware that recovery is possible. I also began to take part in family therapy, where he would come round to my house and talk to my family about my mental illness. Those meetings were very important because my mum and dad were told how my illness works and what it means so they can be more self-assured about looking after me.

Five years ago I was told I should get more involved in doing activities. Before I had my medication changed I just fell asleep all the time and couldn't get out of the house. Staying indoors with the blinds shut was just creating a downwards spiral. My dad also wanted me to get off the sofa and get involved in doing something. So I started attending day centres, which has helped in my recovery. I used to go to the Shore Centre in Brixton and the Mosaic Clubhouse where you can do work or use the canteen. A psychiatric nurse also sent me to a training unit for mentally ill people in Southwark called the Blackfriars Settlement. I tried woodwork and wasn't much good at that but I did like going there. I enjoyed working in the business unit, doing typing and word processing. It's important for professionals to send you to places like this because it gets you involved in something.

Looking back on how I've been treated by mental health professionals in general, I think perhaps some doctors could have been less severe. I felt quite threatened by a doctor at one point who seemed strict and angry with me. At the time I was quite unwell and was quite scared. They could try and appreciate that having a mental illness doesn't automatically make you stupid. It's quite possible to be very clever when you have a mental illness. I'd like to see doctors and other mental health workers appreciating the potential for intellect when talking to their patients. I also think they should explore one's childhood and its relationship to mental illness more as part of a person's treatment. When I was a child I was very badly bullied at primary school and think perhaps that could have caused this illness. The voices in my case are bullying voices and maybe you can trace that back to long ago. I'd like to explore some of this so I could wash it away.

Transition towards recovery

My recovery from mental illness started as soon as I left hospital. I have loved writing poetry since I was a young lad and an important step was being able to do this again. Writing poetry is purifying and makes me happy. During my untreated illness I was writing drivel on bits of dirty paper. But as soon as I was treated my poetry became lucid, free from the confusion caused by mental illness and fit to be published again. My psychologist helped me get back to writing poetry that was more sensitive, sensible and less surreal. Now I've written thousands of poems and had quite a few published in books and magazines. I've got a diploma in Poetry from the Open University and have done public readings at the Poetry Café in Covent Garden and two gigs at the Bread and Roses pub in Clapham. I do loads of writing and get a real rush from it, completing about 40 poems a week, as well as articles and short stories. Perhaps by writing, I am trying to prove I am clever. When the voices are constantly saying that I am no one, writing proves otherwise. When poems are written, cleverness kicks in and the voices wither. By inspiring my intellect, poetry helps to fight my illness.

Developing my own systems for getting rid of symptoms has also helped me improve. Usually I can just get up in the morning without suffering but if the voices do come back I scorn them and turn the other cheek. I can't be bothered to listen to them anymore. By doing the opposite to what the voices tell me to do, I try and win against the illness. I can't do anything else but at the moment that works. I've grown used to some of the comments the voices make and take them with a pinch of salt. Several years ago they would have upset me but now I ignore them and they weaken. This has happened through a process of self knowing and understanding the faults in my own personality. The idea that I can get over these symptoms and won't always be trapped in them appeals to me a great deal.

Making recovery a reality

I consider recovery as a kind of stepping stone towards a better and less insane life. I'm aware that recovery is an issue that is under debate but I'm led to believe that I could be completely recovered in ten years time if I continue with the same rate of progress and continue taking my medication. Only the truly cynical would not believe recovery is possible. Every day my desire to be well and healed of the illness grows more and more and I want saneness above all things. The buzz I get from challenging my illness with sane thoughts and feelings makes me happy. A sane mind is a sort of temple for me, in which my thoughts are cleansed of interference. Recovery means I am freed from hallucinations and can think in bed without hearing things which are simply not there. It means peace and quiet.

Complete recovery for me would mean I could leap out of bed, go to the Job Centre and get a job. I don't like not working because it's like being retired very young. The worst thing about psychosis is that one cannot do a days work and it's instinctive to want to get a job. I know most people say they would like to live on a desert island but it's detrimental to be unemployed for too long. At the moment I can't hold down any kind of paid job – my illness precludes that – but I continue with my writing on a regular, organised basis and this helps me feel very optimistic about the future.

My father is the person who has assisted me most in my recovery. Without my dad I'd be dead in my opinion. All these years of support he's given have been very important. There is this idea that father and son don't get on, but we do. My illness would have surely have remained full blown without him. He helped in having me Sectioned and has helped me put my symptoms in perspective. The time we have spent together discussing my illness has helped me a lot. I tell him about my hallucinations and delusions, he reasons with me about them and we try and understand what they are about. His assistance and advice have aided me for many years.

I'm aware that I am improving within myself and my mind is mended bit by bit. So my life is pretty full these days. I walk for about two miles a day and do lots of cooking and cleaning. I used to be quite fat but have tried to lose weight by eating healthily and taking exercise. I like having a pint of beer a day down the boozer. Four years ago I had an irrational fear of people but now I'm happy to sit and talk to anyone now. I talk to my friend Dan who's given me very valuable support and will speak to me for hours on end about my illness. He's got a qualification in mental health and tries to help me understand what's going on. He was studying for a Master's degree and I visited him for a few days at university without difficulties. Now I can also follow the television and radio correctly when a couple of years ago it was impossible. Lots of my problems were with the television or radio because I'd put them on and hear impossible broadcasts but I can focus on them now without getting lost in thought or imagining things. I feel more connected to the world, have a better concentration span and can think more clearly. This is a sign that recovery is affecting me more and more.

The belief that I have a role to play in public and others people's lives has been hugely important in my recovery. It gives me a sense of purpose and proves I'm a relevant person, which weakens the illness. I'm dying to help other people. My sister has two little children who I really like looking after and I also help to look after my dad as he's getting on in years now. It's so important to contribute to the system one is being affected by, which is why I like to be involved in recovery projects like the book and film. If you are selfish too often, mental illness can start to possess the whole mind.

Hope

My hope is that my illness will continue to weaken more and more. My hope for humanity is that medicine will advance over the years and eventually topple mental illness. It's good to have the hope that over time medicine will improve and the illness will decline and eventually stop. My hope is that people's experience of mental illness will lead to a greater understanding of the way the mind works. As the old systems for treating mentally ill people change there will be more living in the community, and that's progress.

Fortunately I've never felt hopeless and have always had fresh hope. This springs from receiving the right treatment for my mental illness and improving steadily over the years. Ultimately my hope is that through recovery and living healthily – such as stopping smoking and eating less fat - I will live to a ripe old age.

Reflection

I'm glad that I can talk about my illness at length. I imagine if you can't express what's happening in your own head, you will end your days in a psychiatric hospital. You have to interact and listen. My advice for anyone with mental illness is simple. I would tell them to cooperate with treatment and to get it fast. I would implore them to never suffer like I did before I was treated. Explore which medication is right for you. I would never ask anyone to do without medication because you could get ill again. I am cynical about the anti-medication movement and I don't quite understand how one could do without one's tablets.

Before I was ill I was ignorant, but mental illness has changed me. I understand now what I am meant to be doing for the world and people who know me, which is to help, aid, assist and make things work. The illness has caused an awareness that I used to be very selfish but it's made me less so. The most important thing it's taught me is that other people matter no end.

Conclusion

There is still a lot of stigma around mentally ill people and the idea persists that a schizophrenic is a mad axeman. I imagine those are still the beliefs of the general public and don't think that will ever change. Thankfully I haven't experienced much stigma myself and have been treated very well, but I can imagine it's always there. I wish the general public were more aware of the true nature of schizophrenia and what it entails for sufferers and their families. I would like to see a better understanding of mental illness in general and my illness in particular. I want to live in a world where schizophrenia is shoved on the dust heap. I want my illness crushed and the fragments rubbished.

The Schizoid Spreading
(after Philip Larkin's poem 'The Whitsun Weddings')

'All year, inside the sprawled minds that swept
For centuries inland,
A low and sloping word was routeward kept.
Loud skies went by, thought-straddled battles and
Endless voices floating on a cough.
A rattle smashed completely: pleasures dipped
And died; and now and then a spell of sparks
Defaced each week of beauty, truth and wrath,
Until the endless year, now crudely stripped,
Encroached upon a hospital of stars.

At first, I did not notice what a noise
This madness made
Each patient that I stopped at: time deploys
The dints of mental illness like a grave.
And round steeled wards, the groans and skirls
I took for porters hissing in their veils,
And went by pleading. Once I had slept there though,
I heard them, grimacing and screaming: girls
In pastiched torrid clothing, heels and nails,
All drugged completely, watching me flail,

As if out on the end of a vengeful scent,
Raving and complaining
At something which denied *them*. Lost, I bent
Backwardly and forwards, now defamed,
And heard the horror once again and shrill:
The brain with bad welts beneath its boots
And furrowed foreheads; nurses proudly cracked;
An Empire shouting *Slut!*; and then the ferns,
The spitting gloves and tablets on the rack,
The cocoa, coffee; medicated flaps

Marked off from me, who was now all adrift.
Yes, from ward to ward
And white-coats by the yard, and naked breasts
In the hands of directives, these schizoid shores
Were bleating like a fiend. All down this mind
Fixed children danced abroad: my rest was ground,
My pale complexion lost and always blown,
And, as I moved, each waif seemed to define
Just what I saw contorting: nurses frowned
At something killed; doctors assumed the real?'

Copyright James Bellamy 2004

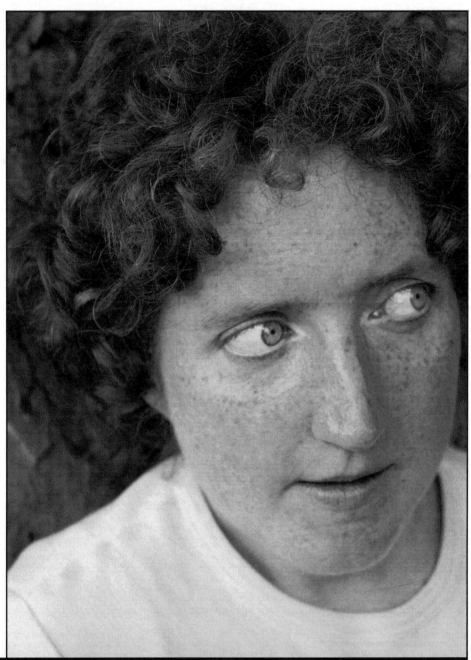

Living By Her Own Rules

Photo: Jane Fradgley

Chapter 10

Living By Her Own Rules

Helen George, 30, of Peckham, South London, is a writer whose first experience of psychosis was part of an intense spiritual awakening. Since then, she has developed her own set of rules for living with psychosis which have helped in her recovery.

Background

I was born in Great Yarmouth and attended a primary school in Lowestoft, then went on to study four A levels at a Catholic high school in Norwich. These included theology, which was challenging and I really enjoyed. Afterwards I went to Liverpool John Moore's University to do a BA degree in Literature, Life and Thought and an MA degree in Creative Writing. Before the MA I took two years out to save up money and get better at writing. During this time, I worked for Liverpool Learning Partnership which was part of the city's education and skills department. Half my time was spent giving out grants to projects and the other half was doing research into education across Liverpool and Merseyside. It was a good job which I accidentally fell into through temping and I absolutely loved it. The MA course was part time on Wednesday evenings but they wanted the same amount of work as if it was full time and we were told to write every day. Doing two part time jobs plus an MA in the evenings, and voluntary work for a domestic violence group a couple of nights a week, was very challenging. I was working at the weekend too, with a Sunday job at a library. All these combined led to my stress levels getting higher and higher, plus I was putting a lot of pressure on myself because all my jobs wanted full commitment. Maybe I'm a bit of a workaholic at heart and I find it hard to say no. I was taking on more and more and it just snowballed. On top of that I was drinking a lot when I came home from work to calm down. It started off as a glass of wine with a meal and before I knew it I'd finished the bottle.

Transition towards illness

It's hard to say exactly when I went mad as it happened gradually. Starting my MA was difficult but I was a bit paranoid before then - I'd had a few fallings out with friends and had overreacted to things. Six months before the MA course began, I was living in a shared house with two lads. I was good mates with one of them and we'd go out clubbing together. But he took something from my room without asking and I started thinking he was reading my diaries as well. So I phoned the landlord and got him chucked out of the house, which I will never stop feeling guilty about. I'll never know for sure if he did read my diaries or not, but he knew certain things about me, probably because we were good friends. Looking back, I've accused other people of reading my diaries when I've been unwell since then, which makes me think I was probably unwell at that point.

Realisation of problem

I started my MA course in October and was in hospital six months later, which is quite a sharp decline. To begin with, I didn't hear voices at all but was more paranoid than I'd realised. I'd also found God in a big way - I know that is every psychotic's story. The tutors on my course were both Catholics and in my interview the woman asked if I considered myself to be a Catholic writer. I said no, not really, because I was an atheist and had been for years. But because they were religious, I thought I had to be too. In between the interview and turning up on the course I built up this thought that she had picked me because I was a Catholic writer and was going to be her protégée. But when I arrived, she treated me just like anyone else and I started worrying that it was because I didn't believe in God. So I started to believe in Him. I had this amazing moment driving to work when I turned a corner, saw a tree lit up by the sunlight and thought, "There has to be a God". This was a genuine spiritual experience but it developed into a delusion. I began to think the tutors on my course were part of a group of nuns and priests who didn't actually want to be part of the Catholic Church and I was the Chosen One who had to save the world. So I had to storm the Vatican to get rid of the Pope and create a new Church. Then I started having absolutely beautiful visions of the Virgin Mary, the most beautiful experiences I've ever had.

Most religious people have got a bit of psychosis in them, because whatever part of the brain makes you psychotic also makes you religious. I read an interesting book called *Psychosis and Spirituality* (Clarke, 2001), which says the only difference between a religious experience and a psychotic experience is that the psychotic person can't cope. That's what I think happened to me, it was just too overwhelming for me. People say to me if I'd been born in 1400 it would have been a completely different story and I probably would have been a mystic and locked myself away like Julian of Norwich. But I'm comfortable with my spirituality now. It's taken me a long time but I would say I was spiritual rather than religious.

By February I was hearing voices. The tutors on my course became voices in my head telling me I was the new Joan of Arc. So I cut my hair off with the kitchen scissors, turned up at university completely bald and said, "See, I've done it!" but they just looked at me. What they were saying in my head didn't fit with what they were saying in reality. So that made me very stressed and I thought they were testing me. Then the voices put me on trial and tried to drown me in a bath as a witch.

Crisis points

So I was stark raving mad but my flatmates hadn't noticed. They thought I was eccentric - which I am quite - but this was actual clinical madness. My friend from Lowestoft had come to visit me and when I told her that I had voices in my head she said that wasn't right. Then I told her I was going to be a nun – she was very religious so I thought she'd be on my side with it – but she insisted we go and see a doctor. I'd moved from being the Chosen One to the voices telling me I was God by that point. So when we went to the walk-in health centre in town I said to the doctor there, "I think I'm God". Then the voices changed and told me I had to go to the mental hospital where there I would spend my 40 days and nights in the desert like Jesus. So I was up for going to hospital, which was quite lucky really. They kept me in the crisis room for many hours then finally I got taken to the Broadoak Acute Unit at Liverpool Hospital. After that it was all a bit of a blur.

Contact with services and treatment

Before I got to the hospital they gave me some pills to stop the voices and help me sleep, as I was still having visions of the Virgin Mary. When I woke up it was quite stark and terrifying to realise I was in a mental hospital. But it was also a relief that there was a way out of being the Chosen One and my delusions. That yes, I'd actually gone mad.

The first night they put me on the worst ward, where lots of people thought they were God. Some of them were pacing up and down and it was a bit scary. As I was under observation, I wasn't allowed off the ward. This was horrible as I just wanted to be outside. A week later I was moved to a ward downstairs but I didn't like that so much because there was no window, just a curtain round my bed. I was still writing every day and wanted to sit and write by the window. I've still got what I wrote then and it seems really interesting to me now because I actually think I was quite sane at that point.

As soon as I realised I was mad I was willing to relook at every part of my thoughts and be told which ones were mad and which weren't. I'm now trying to recognise when I'm mad myself.

I was in hospital for a week before being discharged into my parents' care. But I only stayed with them for a week because I wanted to go back to work and my life in Liverpool as it was before. So I tried to bounce back but I'm not sure how well I did. I took two months off work on full pay and attended a day hospital, then eventually went back to work part time and back to my MA. The olanzapine I was taking made me sleep until three in the afternoon every day, so when I went back to work they put me on aripiprazole and I was well on that for years. My psychiatric nurse came round once a week and I saw the psychiatrist every couple of months. They looked after me really well and if it seemed like I was slipping, they caught me. During this time I managed to finish my MA and I'm really proud of that.

Eventually I decided to do a gap year volunteering in America so I discussed it with my psychiatric nurse. She said there was no reason why I shouldn't because I seemed quite recovered, as long as I kept taking my medication. In America I got a job in a residential community for people with learning disabilities on an organic farm. It was working 16-hour shifts, five days a week, and living in a house with the people with severe learning disabilities. I had to get them up in the morning, change their sheets as two out of four of them were incontinent every day, work on the farm, then cook dinner and put them to bed. It was a long day, a bit like having kids. For the first few months I coped well and then it took its toll on me. I was seeing a girl there in secret, because she didn't want people to know she was gay and I think that made me really paranoid. I'd also slipped out of taking my meds every day, because I needed to be on the ball and they were making me sleepy. So I was starting to get unwell again, but managed to keep from cracking up too much by seeing a psychiatrist there and upping my meds.

After a year in America, I moved to London because I didn't want to go back to Liverpool. Lots of my friends had slipped into doing drugs including those I'd met in the mental hospital. Cocaine is easy to get hold of in Liverpool and really cheap. I wasn't getting much writing done as I was taking drugs myself. But I wanted to do something with my life, not just have a good time. So I moved to London to do care work, which came with free accommodation. I really enjoyed it but I had decided to stop taking my medication suddenly without telling anyone. As I'd not been that well in America, I thought it wasn't doing anything to help me anyway. I was off my medication for nine months when I really cracked up and was very nearly hospitalised. I'd lost my job because I couldn't cope anymore, so I lost my home as well and was basically on the street or staying on people's couches, which was very stressful. At that time I was seeing a trainee psychiatrist and a psychiatric nurse at the community mental health team (CMHT) in Streatham. I refused to be hospitalised so they said they'd give me a couple more days to take my medication and sort myself out. In those two days I managed to get a job with the mental health charity Creative Routes which enabled me to find somewhere to live.

About a month later I went back on my medication and they discharged me because they said I was well, but I actually wasn't at all. Most people are hospitalised in London so everybody knows how unwell they are but I'd come through the system strangely - from Liverpool via America. Also I'm quite articulate and "present well", as they call it, so I didn't come across as mad as I was. I became very unwell and it was only through the support network that I had through my mental health charity work that I stayed out of hospital.

In 2008 I got referred to another CMHT and that's where I was diagnosed schizophrenic. It was absolutely horrible and changed everything. I'd been psychotic for years and not had a problem with it but then I got this schizophrenia label. It's not a word I'm comfortable with. I don't mind calling myself a psychotic, but a schizophrenic has horrible connotations. I should embrace it really but people's reactions to it are so strong. I'm doing voluntary work at the moment and I've said I have mental health problems but if they enquire any more I just tell them I don't want to talk about it. So I'm still trying to come to terms with the diagnosis myself.

At the moment I would say I am quite recovered and have been for a couple of months now. There are good days and bad days but nothing like as bad as when I was off my meds. Medication does help my illness. It zonks me out and because the cogs of my mind are working so much slower, I don't have a chance to get lost in a thought. But I'd like to come off completely because it slows me down so much. What I'm thinking of doing is three months on and three months off to give me a bit of time to be clear headed. The fogginess just gets me down and when people are talking to me I struggle to understand them. Sometimes people have to click their fingers at me to get my attention and my eyes don't move as much, they just stare straight ahead which I hate. So I don't like the medication at all and if I can come off it for at least part of each year then I'll be happy.

Contact with mental health professionals

In Liverpool I had a brilliant psychiatric nurse who would come over and bring my medication to keep me compliant. She was the best psychiatric nurse I've had and really down to earth. We'd sit and have coffee and I could tell her anything because I didn't feel judged by her. She helped me organise going to America and didn't think it was too much for me, didn't patronise me and looked at my strengths rather than my weaknesses.

Since I've been in London I've not had the same level of care. I got discharged from a CMHT at a time when I really could have done with the support, and time proved that I wasn't well. I wish I'd been given the choice to come off medication by the psychiatrist and psychiatric nurse. Whenever I come off the medication I get withdrawal symptoms that are very similar to the illness itself, so I needed more time to sort myself out. I regret that my only choice was to take the medication or go into hospital.

The Social Inclusion, Hope and Recovery Projects team in Lambeth, that runs activities like swimming and healthy eating, is good. I've done psychotherapy, gardening and smoking cessation therapy there. My smoking cessation therapist is by far the best medical professional I've ever met because she treats me like a person first. You hear that so many times but very few people know how to put it into practise.

Sometimes I find mental health professionals a bit patronising and they underestimate my intelligence. Getting called to see the psychiatrist is a bit like being called to the headmaster's office. They go through all these questions and it's really obvious that it's not about you but they are just ticking boxes. It's also important to gain people's trust first. The people I've told everything to - like my psychotherapist - are those who seemed to be having a chat with me rather than talking down to me.

Transition towards recovery

My illness goes in waves and is very much stress-related. The last time I cracked up was because I moved house which wasn't through choice. My housing is very important and I'm much more well when I'm in a house where I'm comfortable. I'd been off my medication for quite some time and been well, then as soon as the stress of moving happened I couldn't cope and had a psychotic episode. It's also related to how I deal with people too. I'm not very good in groups and I like my privacy. When I was in America I lived in a small community of about nine houses and it was too much for me. Voluntary work is quite stressful too because that's about working with a group of people. If I was able to interact with large groups of people without feeling paranoid, I'd know I'd recovered. So stress hinders my recovery but I don't think you can avoid it. Life is stressful and I'm not going to go out of my way to wrap myself in cotton wool. It's learning to deal with life and you've just got to get on with it or you'd end up never leaving the house. I know people who do that and it's not much of a life.

But I think I am recovering. I was determined that it was possible from the start and that my illness wasn't going to get the better of me although it nearly has done a couple of times. The more I learn about my illness the better, because I become more aware of the dangers. At the moment I'm doing mindfulness therapy which is about controlling bad symptoms and keeping me on an even keel with stress. Mindfulness is about learning to see that you don't have to go off with your thoughts, you can just observe them. I really rate it very highly. I've also had cognitive behavioural therapy which was all right and the "worry form" my therapist gave me was helpful. It makes you think about what the worst is that can happen, what the best is that can happen and what is likely to happen. It's absolutely fantastic for dealing with worries and has helped me come a long way in learning to recognise I'm worrying about stuff. Yoga has also really helped me to balance myself.

Making recovery a reality

Having a good support network is the most important thing in my recovery. My family and partner have been very supportive which is fantastic considering what I've put them through. Some of my delusions have led me to say terrible things to my parents and my partner. When I look back, I think I would rather be drugged up to the eyeballs and not be able to speak to anyone than put them through that again.

Day to day I live by rules on voices, religion and paranoia that I have mostly written myself. For example, my rule on religion is an important one because sometimes I think God has told things specifically to me. But I know now I'm not the Chosen One. The Universe, its laws and its Creator are far bigger than me and I am not able to understand them. Now I can see I have the same amount of answers as anyone else and I've stopped trying to learn the truths from God. I used to spend a lot of time trying to tap into other people's thoughts but I've got a rule about that now too. Now I know that just because I watch people and can pick up signals doesn't mean I can sense what they are thinking right now.

Hope

Hope has been important in my recovery although it's such a hard concept to put into words. I remember at school the nuns saying to us that hope is the one thing that human beings should keep in their hearts, and it's interesting that it's suddenly come up in mental health. I do think it's really important to keep hopeful. The opposite of hope is despair and I've managed to avoid that so far. I'm a "glass half full" kind of person and have managed to hang onto that which is good. Sometimes you can forget that there is light at the end of the tunnel.

My hopes for the future are to continue with my writing and get some kind of job. I'm volunteering at the moment and finding my paranoia hard to deal with so if I can get over that hurdle then hopefully I can go back to working in a paid job. Hopefully I'll get to a point where I can live without many symptoms at all. I'd also like to travel around India and go and see the Sistine Chapel in Rome.

Reflection

Having psychosis has taught me that actually I'm not the terrible person I thought I was. It's taught me that I'm too hard on myself and this idea that I'm the Chosen One is really just about being a perfectionist. I'm easier on myself than I used to be. People aren't judging me against this perfect person that I should be and actually they don't mind that I'm not perfect at all. I'm a more secure person because I've sorted out my spirituality problems and know what I believe. Gradually I'm getting to be more grounded. After each episode I know myself better and have learned something good about myself.

Psychosis helped me to get off the treadmill I was on, because I would have carried on being a workaholic and something would have gone wrong at some point. I think I'm a more creative person now and I have time for myself a bit more.

Conclusion

A lifetime of psychotic episodes gets you down. There was a time when I joked about "When I was mad" but now it's a part of my life forever. The idea that it's going to be with me throughout my life is hard to deal with. But recovery is definitely possible for people with psychosis, especially if they pick an aspect of themselves before they were ill that they liked. I've picked writing as something I used to do well, so I'm using that to get back to the person I was before. People who have become ill with psychosis should get back to doing stuff as fast as they can to help them recover. The longer you're off work and you put off socialising the harder it is, so going back to things gradually is a good idea. Also remember who you were before you went mad and know that you can be that person again.

Reference

Clarke I (ed) (2001) *Psychosis and Spirituality: Exploring the New Frontier.* Whurr Publishers, London.

Mental Health Revolutionary

Photo: Jane Fradgley

Chapter 11

Mental Health Revolutionary

Gordon McManus, 58, from Tulse Hill, South London, was an activist in the British Communist movement when he developed psychosis that lasted for 20 years. A process of writing and therapy enabled him to begin recovery. He has developed a definition and model of recovery that has since been widely used by mental health professionals and service users.

Background

I was born in Burma in 1952 and moved to the UK with my family at the age of 12. We lived in South London and I went to school in Tulse Hill, which was a real racial and political melting pot. I am from a mixed-race background myself – my father is Irish Burmese and my mother is a Dutch-Spanish-Portugese-Sinhalese mix – but I was different from the Indians, Pakistanis and West Indians at my school. I'd never met a Black person until I went to school but was immediately attracted to their culture because they had just arrived in Britain and spoke Patois. If you couldn't speak English at school you were sent into the educationally subnormal class. This injustice disturbed me and I wanted to get rid of it by fighting for the Black students' rights. The British Black Consciousness political movement was active in Brixton at the time, which was a hub of activity. It was a beautiful community and at school I became friends with its future leading lights, including activist and broadcaster Darcus Howe and poet Linton Kwesi Johnson. This generation brought Black politics into South London and my time spent among them was also to be my political cradling. Although I knew about Harold Wilson, I was not interested in British politics and there were no Black people of any kind in the Labour Party. When I got to college to study A levels, I became treasurer of the first Black Student Society at further education level in Britain.

In 1974 I went onto the University of Essex to study Linguistics with Sociology. It was one of the most politically radical universities in Britain at the time. The anarchist group The Angry Brigade were students there and police were everywhere. They knew I was politically radical too so I think they marked my card. This is when my struggle with mental health problems, particularly paranoia, started. I was elected chair of the Third World First Society, bringing speakers in from the African National Congress and Palestine, and was a founder member of the university's first Black Student Society. In my final year the university authorities tried to turn me into a State agent. I wanted to do my thesis on the Jamaican Creole language but the Linguistics department said I couldn't because they didn't have academics specialising in the subject. The Head of Department asked me if I would research and write about the language Black people used when they played dominoes. He wanted me to translate their Patois and present my findings to the police. In return, the department offered me a scholarship to Georgetown University in Washington. But it would have been a betrayal and I couldn't do it, so I refused in a polite way. Instead, I did my own thing but eventually came away with a third class degree. I was on for a first or 2.1 but think I got marked down because I wouldn't work for the police.

I was very angry with the university and the department of Linguistics about my final mark so I decided to become a revolutionary and overthrow them. After graduating, I started to read the work of Marx and Engels and became attracted to the Communist philosophy. This is primarily about the freedom of mankind to develop his creative ability to its fullest extent while labouring for society and his just rewards. I was on the dole and finding it hard to get a job, so in 1979 decided to train as a teacher. Throughout the 1980s, I taught business studies at secondary school level but I didn't want a career in teaching, just to be able to make enough money so I could carry out my political activities. The students knew I was into Leftist politics but I didn't carry this into the classroom.

Transition towards illness

In 1980 I became a Communist when I joined the New Communist Party (NCP), which was formed in 1977 after breaking away from the Communist Party of Great Britain. This was against the wishes of my family and friends, including those in the Black community. Their objection was that the Communists had done nothing for Black people and their struggle against oppression. But it was the right place for me to go to become a revolutionary in this country at the time. The touchstone of Communism in the 1980s was whether you followed the Soviet model, and the NCP was both pro-Soviet and pro-Stalinist. So I became engaged full time in political activism for the NCP, but it turned out to be mundane and disastrous. Their biggest political activity was running a stall at a flea market in Putney to raise money for the Party. They were like a sect, isolated and on the fringes of political society. There was distrust and paranoia everywhere, with everyone watching everyone else to see if you were a police agent. In 1981, I was expelled from the NCP along with a few other people due to ideological differences. I joined the newly-formed Communist group Proletarian in 1982 as one of its leaders and was involved for about seven years as an activist and educator. Here I worked on the Irish National Question and the anti-Apartheid issue, becoming Chair of Lambeth Anti-Apartheid group. It was horrendous to be a Communist in the 1980s and this is part of what made me ill. There was a lot of bitterness in Proletarian, with people fighting power struggles and watching each other. It had turned a bit cultish and they wanted members to give their life to the cause. Eventually I got thrown out of Proletarian due to a policy disagreement. My relations with the anti-Apartheid movement had also soured by this point because someone told me my name was in disrepute among them. I was furious at having been treated so badly by both groups and this caused the paranoia to return, triggered by all the stress. The Communist movement had crippled me but I couldn't go back into the Black community and tell them what had happened.

Realisation of problem

I left politics completely in 1987 and it felt like I had lost my reason for being. This triggered a mental breakdown which began with whispers, then developed into abusive political voices and hallucinations including a visual form called Mugabe telling me not to use books and telephones. Although I didn't know it, I became ill with schizophrenia in 1991 but I thought it was the Soviets controlling me. For ten years, I lived under the delusion that they had developed a new science of mental telepathy and were using it to try and communicate with me. A friend got someone he knew who had done a PhD at the University of Moscow to check whether this was possible. He told me that the Soviets didn't have that kind of science and that it couldn't be done, saying he thought I had a few loose screws. But I didn't break the delusion for several more years and continued to live with paranoia.

Crisis points

I was fully schizophrenic from 1993 to 2005. During this time I had five breakdowns and was hospitalised four times, twice under a Section of the Mental Health Act. In 1993, I broke down with the symptoms of paranoid delusions, voices and visual hallucinations. I was Sectioned for the first time because I'd been carrying knives and my brother called the police, who came and took me to hospital. In 1994, I broke down again and was hospitalised at the South Western Hospital in Stockwell. In 1995, I was admitted to hospital voluntarily for a few weeks because I couldn't cope with the voices. For the next five years, I managed not to break down while living with schizophrenia, but was hospitalised again in 2000. When I came out in 2001, I'd lost my intellectual functioning and couldn't even write - someone even had to fill out forms for me. This made me think I couldn't go on living like that any more so I tried to rebuild my life and capabilities. My sister had given me a computer so I tried to help myself by using it to write and play chess. During this period, I only told one friend about my mental illness and this was a source of comfort. But the voices were so severe I broke down again and was rehospitalised in 2002 for a few months. I had finally been diagnosed with paranoid schizophrenia, despite having hidden the symptoms from my family and the doctors for a long time. I refused to take the medication I was given. At first the doctors said I had paranoid psychosis because I refused to tell them I was hearing voices and seeing forms. I didn't care because I was more concerned with the delusion about the Soviets. Another doctor said he couldn't diagnose me because I wasn't talking to him, so I thought I'd better come out and express what was happening to me. This openness meant I was no longer under stress to hide my illness. It helped me begin to recover and stay well because my family and the doctors were at last able to understand my problems.

My last hospital admission was in 2003 and I've not had a breakdown since then. I am now on the medication risperidone which has made me much calmer but I still live with hearing voices and seeing forms. Sleeping is difficult because the voices can keep me awake at night but usually I manage to get a few hours. The voices then wake me up at around 5am and last for three hours. This makes me depressed as it's no way to wake up in the morning. However, I'm able to cope with the symptoms better now and they usually disappear by 9am so I can get on with my day.

Contact with services and treatment

For 12 years, I'd been under the medical model of treatment but the psychiatrist decided that drugs alone weren't working. So I was recommended for cognitive behaviour therapy at the Maudsley Hospital psychosis clinic. This was very helpful in enabling me to talk about my condition instead of keeping it in my head. It removed a lot of stress and helped me begin to recover. My second period of therapy has been with a clinical psychologist at Streatham Community Mental Health Team (CMHT). This gave me someone to talk to about my problems on a fortnightly basis which helped stave off hospitalisation and another breakdown. He gave me papers to study on recovery by psychologists who have experienced mental health problems themselves, including Patricia Deegan, Peter Chadwick and Rachel Perkins. But although I was reading their definition of recovery, they didn't sort out my problems and I had to find out what it meant for me. So I developed a model of my own recovery process to help me structure and rationalise my illness.

The model shows a journey from normality, through hospital breakdown and schizophrenia, into a stage of recovery which hopefully leads back to a period of normal life. This has been very useful for enabling me to rebuild myself. We presented some of these ideas about recovery to the recovery group which is regularly held at the CMHT. On one occasion, the psychologist asked the audience to come up with a succinct definition of recovery. He now uses my definition, "Coping with your illness and trying to have a meaningful life", at workshops and in his writing, which I find embarrassing and flattering. I also took part in a film and book on recovery which was produced by another service user for the South London and Maudsley NHS Foundation Trust. Doing those interviews was also very important in helping me rationalise my illness. My psychologist now says I'm three-quarters of the way recovered and we are now working on a book on my recovery together.

Contact with mental health professionals

I have been lucky and am quite happy with the good treatment I've received from mental health professionals. Doctors, psychiatrists and social workers have all Sectioned me which I resented at first because I wanted to be cared for in the community, not in hospital. Then I eventually came to an understanding that they were right and were concerned about me. When I was hiding the illness, they didn't know what to do with me. In those days you only had a social worker or a psychiatric nurse who would come and see you. The psychiatric nurse would be sitting in my front room while I'd be hearing voices and she just didn't know what to say. But since I started talking about it things improved. Professionals have to know how to bring the service user out of themselves more. They need to understand how individuals express themselves because some people won't talk about their illness. It's their job to try and make the person realise that they are suffering from an illness. Recovery becomes easier once you confront the illness.

The contact with mental health professionals that led to my recovery began in 2001, when I had been living with constant symptoms of schizophrenia but hadn't told anyone. The police caught me carrying a knife again and I was taken to court, where the duty solicitor argued that I was mentally ill. The Magistrate put me in hospital which is where I first told a psychiatrist that I was hearing voices and seeing forms. He diagnosed me as having paranoid schizophrenia which was a shock. It freaked me out because you don't see yourself as long-term mentally ill until you are categorised that way. But it destroyed the delusion that the Soviets had a new mental science which they were using to try and communicate with me. The psychiatrist helped me a lot by enabling me to confront the fact that I was mentally ill and then the process of recovery could begin. He also stopped me from being evicted from my flat which prevented me from becoming homeless. I'd been hiding my illness so well that the Benefits Agency thought I could work again. They stopped my housing benefit and income support and I was in rent arrears. But my psychiatrist got the Judge to sort it out for me. In 2006, a psychiatric nurse referred me to the clinical psychologist which was a further bridge to my recovery. The psychologist changed my life completely by helping me to confront and rationalise my illness.

Transition towards recovery

Recovery is an approach to your mental health problems rather than a cure. It began for me in 2006 when I started having therapy at the Maudsley Hospital. Until then, no one had ever spoken to me fully about my illness and I was able to discuss it for the first time with the therapist. Then I met my psychologist and I started to learn about the experiences of other people who had written about their illnesses. Instead of being a schizophrenic I felt like a psychology student! At first I didn't understand and it took me over a year before I got to grips with it. Recovery became an intellectual process for me and that helped me a lot.

Making recovery a reality

Now I am going through the beginning of the endgame with my illness. I am aiming to win this game through a process of recovery. The schizophrenia does not affect me day and night anymore and there are periods when I can think clearly enough to work things through. I started doing this by spending the time since my last admission from hospital researching and writing a book on globalisation. This has helped to get rid of the political voices and reconstruct my reality by developing my own theoretical understanding of Socialism and Capitalism. I also started to hold domino sessions at my flat every two weeks with a group of friends, who only found out I had schizophrenia in 2007. These sessions and friends have helped my recovery a lot because they gave me regularity, sociality and distract me from living a schizophrenic life. I've also got my coping strategies, including using the television, writing and playing chess to distract myself from the voices and forms. One of my friends has set up a politics website for me and I now have a monthly news sheet where I can publish my own political views and analysis. This has brought me back to life. I don't internalise politics in my head any more, because I use these outlets to objectify my political thoughts and understanding which gives me a sense of reality. I try to stay stress-free and do the things that contribute towards my wellbeing such as through good relationships with friends and family. In recovery you've got to work at your relationships. My family had problems with my being a Communist but I have worked hard to rebuild that in the last three or four years. I am still very reclusive but I do that deliberately. I don't want too many things on my plate because I can become overstressed and have a relapse. So I keep things to a minimum and hope that will help me rebuild and prevent me from having another breakdown. I've worked really hard and made good progress.

Even though I was a late onset schizophrenic I still have a chance to fully recover. Recovery is possible and I'm going to use whatever means necessary to prove this to the doctors. In my case, it's taking a long time and is a slow process. My recovery model is a continuum along which you can go back as well as forwards. When you get a cold, it goes in a few days but recovery from schizophrenia takes its own course. I know I will have recovered when I am completely free of the voices and the forms. This now happens three or four times a year so I am pleased that I am making progress. It means I am not schizophrenic but in the recovery stage. The worst thing is not being fully free of the symptoms yet, but when I am, I will go and see the psychiatrist and show them that it is possible to recover completely.

Hope

When I first came out of hospital in 2001 and decided to engage in my own recovery process, I didn't realise you needed hope. So I was being optimistic rather than hopeful about becoming fully recovered through writing and playing chess. I nearly lost all hope when I broke down the following year and didn't come out until 2003, and I still despair when I hear voices and see forms. But the concept of hope came into my head as a means of recovery when I entered therapy with my psychologist and read the article *You Need Hope to Cope* by Rachel Perkins (2006). I now realise hope is necessary every day as I wake up and have to deal with hearing voices or seeing forms. Writing the books on globalisation and my recovery has given me a sense of hope and got rid of the political voices. They have been important in helping me get my intellectual functioning back again and giving me a goal. If you don't have goals you just sink into your illness. My hope is that I will be fully recovered and free of the symptoms so I can go back to work as a teacher. I want to keep on writing and develop my creativity through the monthly news sheet on my website. I hope to avoid a relapse and break down again. I'm 58 and there isn't much time left for me and the illness has wasted 20 years of my life. But I hope my experiences give hope to other people and help them learn more about their own recovery.

Reflection

Friends of mine tell me I've become an expert in recovery. Well I don't think I'm an expert - all I know is that I've lived through schizophrenia and am coming out of it now. It's very important that other people can learn from my experiences. Recently I did a presentation on my recovery at the CMHT I attend. Later, when I was in hospital getting an injection, I met someone who had seen it who said I'd inspired him. I was so shocked because when you have schizophrenia, you don't see yourself as inspiring others. Talking about my illness is a contribution to the recovery movement though. My psychologist calls me a mental health revolutionary but I didn't mean to be that, even though I did set out to be a revolutionary! The definition of recovery I developed was not meant to be a general working definition for service users and professionals, but to help me gain a better understanding of my illness. I was trying to make sense of what I was going through. The fact that I was able to rationalise my illness like that makes me feel good. But I'm happy for it to be used more widely if it helps someone else to recover.

The most important thing for me is that someone with mental illness confronts it, recognises they have a problem and tries to recover. They should be open and honest about their experience and then it won't take as long to get through it. Treatment of psychosis needs to become more service-user orientated and the person needs to become more involved in their own recovery instead of a psychiatrist telling you what to do. It's important that each service user has their own individual recovery programme so they can judge how well they are doing.

Conclusion

I have lost a third of my life, teaching career, political activity and living a personal life to mental illness. I call them the lost years. But I have learned to fight back and recover fully, having built up a certain amount of resilience in the last 20 years. I can look at myself and say I have survived.

Reference
Perkins R (2006) First Person: You Need Hope To Cope. In: Roberts G, Davenport S, Holloway F and Tattan P (eds) *Enabling Recovery: The Principles and Practice of Rehabilitation*. Royal College of Psychiatrists: London.

A Psychologist's Progress

Chapter 12

A Psychologist's Progress

Emma Harding, 35, from Tooting, South London, developed psychosis while studying for a degree in psychology at university. She recovered and now works as a clinical psychologist for the South London and Maudsley NHS Foundation Trust, specialising in treating people with psychosis.

Background

The first time I realised there was something wrong was on the car journey from my parents' house in Cambridgeshire to start university in Canterbury. Throughout the entire journey, I was crying my eyes out and getting very upset. This was unlike me because I'm normally quite headstrong and independent. I was thinking about my life and going through big emotional changes for the first time. Beginning university just brought everything out in the open and I struggled to settle in. I was living in a shared house and tried to get on with people because I really wanted to fit in. The truth is I'd always felt like a bit of an outsider. We'd moved house from Buckinghamshire to Cambridgeshire when I was 13 and I went from a posh girl's grammar school with a very good reputation to a mixed comprehensive school. All the friends I'd hung out with at home had dropped out of school or had been in prison so it was strange being around well-educated people in Canterbury again. It was a bit of a culture shock which amplified the idea that I didn't fit in. So I tried doubly hard and tried to figure out what people were thinking. I started doing what psychologists call "mind reading" – trying to work out what might be going through other people's heads based on what I was worried about.

Transition towards illness

I was also struggling with my course. This was the first time I'd studied psychology and I felt like I had a lot to catch up on. The amount of maths you needed completely flummoxed me. I'd been used to having teachers running around after me but suddenly I had to motivate myself, work out how to use academic journals and reference essays. It was all too much to handle and I started to deteriorate, getting nervous and paranoid. In classes, it seemed like the lecturers were talking about psychological experiments that had been conducted on people I knew. I thought they were referring to the things that had happened in my life. Once I was in my room and started hearing whispers and reading about hallucinations in my psychology textbooks. Things clearly weren't right so I went to the university counselling service and told them I was hearing voices and couldn't keep up with my work. But it was no help; the counsellor basically said, "Things are really rough for you, why don't you go and bake some cookies?" All the phones for the student nightline service were in public areas so I couldn't ring them up either as I was worried that people could overhear me.

Realisation of problem

At the time I didn't think it was psychosis, though I knew something was badly wrong. One of my tutors had just given a lecture on schizophrenia so I went to see him. He said he didn't think I had it, because most people who did weren't aware of it. But I made an appointment to see the university psychiatrist anyway. I'd begun to think people were plotting against me around the university. I'd had this really bad experience in a lecture when I thought there was a spotlight on me and people were ridiculing me. But I'd got it into my head that I wasn't going to tell the psychiatrist about the paranoia, so I just told him I was depressed and he gave me Prozac. Things had got really bad - I felt like I wasn't going to get through university because I couldn't keep up with the work, I had a failed relationship, I felt like I wasn't getting on with any of the people I was living with and that I wasn't going to have the success I expected and my parents wanted for me. The only thing I could do was end my life. So the Wednesday after I saw the psychiatrist I took an overdose of Prozac and paracetamol.

Crisis points

By Saturday I kept waking up being sick everywhere thinking, I'm still alive and I'm not actually going to die. My housemates had been knocking on my door but I just ignored them. Eventually I thought, fuck it, and called the doctor. She looked at me after she had opened the curtains in my bedroom and said, "When did you turn yellow?" My liver was damaged so I was rushed to the acute hospital in Canterbury then onto King's College Liver Unit in London. In the bed next to me was a man with liver failure through natural causes and every day somebody from his family would come and read to him from the Koran in a bedside vigil. It was really moving. I had caused this myself but this poor person had done nothing to deserve it. While I was there a psychiatrist came to see me and asked if I was going to try and commit suicide again, but I said no.

After I was discharged, I went back to university and kind of got through the year, walking out of some exams and not turning up to others. In summer I went home to my parents but was becoming quite paranoid again. I'd asked my dad to lend me some money because I said I wanted to go to Glastonbury. But actually I bought a ticket and went to Holland because I wanted to check if people in other countries were talking about me. When I got over there, I found out that they actually were!

Back home, old friends would come round but it felt like everyone was laughing at me, so I started withdrawing more and more. The hallucinations and delusions were also getting worse. I started hearing whispers and people singing Shakespearean sonnets outside my bedroom window. At first this sounded really nice, but the whispers became voices and the voices got louder. I also thought I'd developed the power of psychic communication and could make it rain or lamp posts flicker on and off when I wanted. It occurred to me that if I could cause all these amazing things to happen, then I actually must be God. In retrospect, I was in such a bad place emotionally I think I was defending myself, like an oyster covering a grain of grit inside itself with pearl. At first being God was quite nice - I could do things for my mum and dad – but it got worse as I remembered the Bible said I would have to organise doomsday and make decisions about who would live or die.

This went on for a couple of months but no one noticed as I was isolating myself. I'd only go out at night and had put all these scarves and altars up in my bedroom. My friends had given up on me and my parents thought I was just going through some weird teenage rebellion. They only really thought something was wrong when I said to them one day, "I'm God", as if they should have known already. I suppose if you're God you assume people know. At the time I was aware this was going to be a massively important experience in my life, but wasn't sure how or why.

Contact with services and treatment

A couple of days later my dad said he had to go to the doctor about his back and asked me to come with him. So I went and he told the doctor he was really worried about me because I had tried to commit suicide and was saying I was God. The doctor didn't do much, but my dad pushed hard. Within a couple of weeks I was in Hinchingbrooke Hospital in Huntingdon. I was sleeping on a mattress on the floor because I'd dismantled the bed, thinking it was an antenna for evil. I woke up one day to a psychiatrist leaning over me saying, "Emma, I think you've got schizophrenia," but I just said, "I can't have. I'm a psychology student!" By this time it was December 1994 and I should have been in my second year at university. But I was in a psychiatric unit as a voluntary patient until the following February. I only got the official diagnosis of schizophrenia a couple of years later.

To begin with I was taking chlorpromazine but used to wake up on the floor having fainted in the middle of the night. One doctor put me on trifluoperazine (Stelazine) for a couple of years but it gave me tardive dyskinesia, a side effect of antipsychotic medication which makes your body twitch involuntarily. Then I started getting oculogyric crises, where my head and eyes would roll back in jerky movements. Now I'm on olanzapine which works well and hasn't sedated me like it does some people.

Due to the medication, I couldn't hear voices any more and was kind of missing them because I was lonely. But it did help slow my thoughts down and made me realise the size of the mountain in front of me I had to climb. I'd told friends I was in rehab for drug use and convinced myself I had a brain tumour - anything to not admit I had a mental health problem. Loads of other people kept coming into hospital, staying for a couple of weeks then leaving again but it felt like I would be in there forever.

Contact with mental health professionals

The clinical psychologist I saw in hospital was absolutely fantastic and really took me under her wing. She convinced the university to accept me back again to re-sit my exams. Her approach to dealing with me was holistic, she didn't just try to get rid of the delusions or paranoia but asked what direction I valued and how she could get me there. I remember thinking, "I really want to be like you one day". She was very calm and thoughtful and it felt like she really had time for me and believed in me. I could have so easily become voiceless but that psychologist really helped me believe I could do something and had something to offer. She taught me how to approach life again and think a bit more carefully about the direction I was moving in.

Losing touch with the first psychiatrist I saw after my suicide attempt was difficult. I know how hard it is for mental health services when people are moving around the country but I think it's quite worrying that I tried to kill myself and there wasn't much follow-up. Given that I'd taken an overdose it was probably obvious that I needed some help and support. But my dad had to insist really quite fervently that a psychiatrist came to see me after I'd disclosed that I was God.

Transition towards recovery

Things did get better in hospital and I revised really hard for my resits. I'd attend a day centre, go to a yoga class there and then revise solidly for three hours every day. It was one of the best moments of my life when I turned the exam paper over and realised I could actually answer the questions. I'd always been told I had a bright future ahead of me, which is probably why it was so easy to believe I was God! But when I came out of hospital and restarted university, it was like having to learn how to live again. The world seemed massive and I seemed infinitesimally smaller than I had ever been before. I had to fend for myself, do my own cooking and shopping and it felt like I'd never be able to do it. My sleep pattern was terrible but now I had to get up for 9am lectures. I was still struggling with the work and found it quite difficult. Previously my saving grace had been that I had a good memory, but the medication killed it and to this day I have to work really hard to get through. I also needed to get a whole new group of friends, though there were still some people there I'd known in the first year. Some of my friends admitted to me that they thought I was really selfish when they knew me in the first year, but I'd say, "I was having a psychosis, what do you expect? Part of that is thinking you're the centre of the universe!" Through hard work and determination I managed to get my degree. I'd come so close to losing it all that I wasn't going to let it happen again.

At the time I thought I'd quite like to become a psychologist but didn't really know what was involved. My lecturer said not to bother trying to get into clinical psychology because it's difficult, but I definitely wanted to work in mental health. When I left university my dad found an article in *The Times* about South West London and St George's Mental Health NHS Trust, which was specifically looking to employ people with mental health problems as they had something different to offer. A support worker post came up in the Trust so I went for an interview and they offered me the job! Once I started, I was supported by the user employment programme which supports service users working in the Trust. Then I had an accident on my moped and needed to be redeployed within the Trust. So somebody decided to offer me a secondment into the user employment programme and I ended up working there for six years. The job involved promoting employment rights for people with mental health problems. I had to do lots of presentations and public speaking and go to meetings and consultations to advocate for service users' rights. I also had the opportunity to talk about my own experiences. The role meant I was working closely with a psychologist who was really kind to me and got me thinking about my future career direction. She encouraged me to do an MSc in Occupational Psychology, which helped me to learn how to study again. At the time, the mental health charity Rethink was looking for someone to share their experiences of using services so I started working as a media volunteer for them. I did loads of media work and appeared on *Richard and Judy*, *GMTV with Lorraine Kelly* and *Newsnight* talking about mental illness. People used to say I was brave for appearing in the media, but I didn't think so. Working with Rethink also gave me the opportunity to train people involved with mental illness and I trained psychiatrists, drug reps, the Metropolitan Police and Girlguiding UK. I also went to conferences all over

Europe – Hamburg, Lisbon, Brussels – talking about my mental illness.

When I was working at the Trust I used to sit on the user involvement panel for the clinical psychology training course at the University of Surrey. This brought together clinical psychology trainees, tutors, local service users and carers to give their input on the course. One day I happened to mention to a tutor there that I wanted to be a psychologist, so he suggested I apply for clinical psychology training. He said there was nothing wrong with my experience and that they were trying to open the course up to people from non traditional backgrounds. I got on the course and finished my doctorate in 2008. Since then I've been working at the South London and Maudsley NHS Foundation Trust in their psychosis services which are very dear to my heart. This is mainly with people who have psychosis and other problems such as depression, anxiety or drug abuse. I use cognitive behaviour therapy, schema therapy and some psychodynamic ideas. I've started to do some work around the Trust in other user involvement areas, trying to encourage other service users to get involved through the user involvement register. Over the past year I've also been helping the British Psychological Society produce some guidelines for psychologists on service user involvement.

As both a clinician and someone who has experienced psychosis, I get to see things from both sides. Most of the people I work with don't know I've had mental health problems and having only been qualified for two years, I don't know if I'm confident enough to tell them. I don't know if I'd be doing them a disservice because I can never know what someone else is experiencing and don't want them to think my mental health is more important than theirs. But if a member of staff says something I don't agree with, I'm not afraid to challenge how they came to that conclusion. When I was a trainee, I was in a meeting about somebody who had come into the service for the first time. I remember the psychiatrist saying that this person couldn't have severe mental health problems as they were working as a manager. I just thought, how can you say that?

After the huge episode where I went completely over the edge I've stayed really quite well. There have been wobbly times when things got stressful but I've managed to keep it under control. A couple of years ago I decided to change medication because I wanted to lose weight, but the side effects were hideous so I decided to stick to the olanzapine from then on. I haven't had a major episode since.

Making recovery a reality

When I was in hospital, I was always quite hopeful that recovery was a possibility but it really began when I went back to university and challenged myself to learn. Things continued to improve when I started working and could actually use my own experience of mental illness to help other people. The thought I'd had years earlier that I was experiencing something massively important actually turned out to be true. I've learned something from my experiences and I don't have to be ashamed of what I went through.

I don't know if you ever get to a finishing point where you can say you have recovered, it's more of an ongoing journey. There may be times when things aren't going well and you get yourself in a trough, but you have to dig yourself out and move towards where you want to be, even if you don't actually get there. There is a whole trail and tangent of experiences that have led you to wherever you are in life. Recovery is about not becoming jaded but looking to the future and accepting that there are interesting, new things to come.

Having people around you to support you on that journey is important. My parents always had faith in me, which I finally started to have too when I went back to university. The psychologists I met in hospital and at my first job both believed in me and helped me to achieve. Finding my life partner and getting a flat has been massively important in my recovery. Taking responsibility for my life has also helped. I've worked really hard to get where I am and that makes me feel quite positive.

If people with psychosis think recovery is a myth then it's probably not going to happen. But recovery *is* possible and it can happen. If they have hopefulness and optimism then it is more likely to happen as well.

Hope

Hope has been massively important in my recovery – huge amounts of probably unsubstantiated hope. If you are not even a little bit open-minded to hope, you won't get out of bed in the morning. When I took the overdose I was hopeless, thinking there wasn't an area left in my life that wasn't untainted by the horrendous thing that was happening to me. But you need a little bit of hope to make you do things. Even when your job is going badly and your house is about to be repossessed, if you have hope you can use it to infect the other areas of your life.

My hope for the future is to carry on working where I am because I love the Trust and the client group. I also hope the service user guidelines I've been working on get a good reception. When I thought I was God I thought I wanted to cure poverty and disease. I know I can't do that but I can use my experience of surviving psychosis to help other people find their way through. Helping others is the icing on the cake for me, but when other people do well it also reinforces to me that recovery is possible.

Reflection

As a clinician I know a fair bit about psychosis because it's one of the most common mental illnesses and has been widely researched. Psychiatrists and academics used to think that therapy with people who had psychosis couldn't be successful because they are just too chaotic and nonsensical. Psychosis was thought to be simply rubbish from your brain. But I can't just dismiss something that is so integral to somebody's worldview by saying it's just a product of the imagination. Our imaginations are a product of us. Delusions and voices do actually have some basis in our experience and inner thoughts and fears. For example, my thoughts of being God were all really rooted in my experiences of feeling different and not wanting to accept my vulnerability.

Quite often it's the injustice of not being believed or taken seriously that hinders people's recovery. Sometimes I do marvel at the extent to which people ask for help and simply get brushed aside. If we dismiss people because they are mad or have a sensory impairment, we are missing out on a whole universe of human experience which is part of life. The greatest injustice is when people don't get the opportunity to speak up for themselves. Someone I used to work with said it was his job to advocate for what he called "the inarticulate service user". He said everybody should have somebody who stands up for them, but not everybody does. The greatest kindness is when we go the extra mile to help someone.

Conclusion

Mental illness can happen to anybody. I was really shy, but down to earth and sensible, when psychosis came out and tried to eclipse my life. I didn't want it to be the end of my life, though it very nearly was. Psychosis is terrifying but it doesn't mean you have to be on your own. If you can listen to other people's stories or open yourself up to other people's reality, not get rigid in your own mind, it doesn't have to go bad. People are likely to be afraid of psychosis but it doesn't have to win. I'd hope people would look at my experience and see that it takes a lot of help and support to decide where you want to go with your recovery.

Mental illness doesn't make you a bad person or mean your life is over. It's not something people need to be ashamed of or hide behind. It can be something to celebrate that can make your life unique and different.

Everybody has intrusive thoughts or things that frighten them. The more we pretend it's everybody else, we are buying into the lie that you are weird if you have a mental health problem. I don't think mental illness makes me special. It's just a natural part of life and can be a very profound and creative experience.

The Best in Me

Photo: Jane Fradgley

Chapter 13

The Best in Me

Carl Lee, 52, from Brixton, South London, is a musician and songwriter who developed psychosis in his forties. He believes that art and music can be used as a form of self-expression to empower people with mental illness and aid recovery.

Background

I was born in Jamaica to a Jamaican mother and Chinese father and would stay with my grandmother while my parents went to work. She was an extremely religious woman and would send us to church regularly. Here I sang in the choir and started to develop my love of music. My grandmother's faith was not Anglo-Saxon Christianity - she was a member of the Pocomania church which is a Jamaican spiritualist religion. At my grandmother's church I used to see people speaking in tongues and falling over. In 1967, my parents and I moved to the UK and lived in Brixton. I went to school in Clapham and passed the 11 plus to get into grammar school where I enjoyed writing, literature and English. There was an American teacher working at the school who had a lot of faith in me, saw my writing potential and pushed me. Today I still enjoy writing lyrics, songs and poetry. I also loved music, though there wasn't much option to study that at my school. Today I play guitar, keyboard, mouth organ and djembe and bongo drums. Michael Jackson was my inspiration and I dreamed of becoming a pop star like him, even forming my own little pop group with friends. My favourite other artists were soul singers like Sam Cook and Ben E King, and reggae which is part of my Jamaican culture. Mum used to play the music of Billie Holliday, but wasn't too keen on the idea of me becoming a musician. She wanted me to get a career to fall back on, so when I finished school I went to Putney College of Further Education to study Law. From there, I got a job as a solicitor's clerk in Brixton.

Transition towards illness

When I was in my forties, I was in a relationship with a lady and we had a child together. At the time there was a big fuss going on in the media about the MMR vaccination causing autism, so I became quite apprehensive about the child having the injection. When he was three months old, the health worker kept coming round to encourage her to take the child for the injection. But I sat down with him and said there was no way it was going to happen. I'm very sensitive if something feels wrong and wanted to wait until he was older. As I didn't live with this lady I used to go round to her house and visit her, but one day had a very vivid dream. In it, I saw her going to take a plane and pushing the pram to the base of the steps. A tall white gentleman came down the steps of the plane, and she took the child out of the pram and gave it to him. I shouted at her in the dream, saying, "What do you think you're doing? Give me my child!" The man looked at me, smiled wryly and realised I was serious, so stopped trying to take the child. When I woke up out of the dream at one o'clock in the morning I was very worried. So I got up, went round to her house and knocked on the door. She answered and asked me what was wrong. I told her I'd dreamt she was going to give the child away to someone and asked her what she had done with him. She tried to tell me not to be ridiculous, but after I grilled her she admitted she had gone and got him vaccinated. I was very angry with her because we had discussed her waiting until he was older before having it done. Suddenly I heard this vivid voice calling out, "Leave this house immediately, this woman has betrayed you." It told me that she was working with the police and that if I didn't leave straight away, they would come and arrest me. The voice sounded so authoritative and commanding I thought it was the voice of God. It shook my soul - I felt powerless and had to do what it said. The voice told me to go now, so I left her house without my shoes or keys. But it said I was not to go directly home, so I sat outside my house for about an hour. Then at two o'clock in the morning, the voice told me to ring my neighbour and get him to let me in. My neighbour came downstairs and he could see I was distraught. He took me upstairs where I told him about what had happened and that I couldn't go back and get my keys from my girlfriend's house. That was my first psychotic experience.

Realisation of problem

From then on, the voices were very frequent and strong. I also started having visions, where I could see things that other people couldn't see. I could look at a person, see their skeleton and look into their soul. I saw demons and spirits in the room, such as dog men that wore clothes and stood on their hind legs. But I didn't fear these things, because I was so sure that the voice I'd heard was God and He assured me I would be protected. If I didn't have that reassurance, I would have been very scared. As I lived with these visions, I felt my consciousness was opened up and I could see the world in a different light. Now and again I still have these visions today, though not the vivid experience that I had before.

Crisis points

The first time I was hospitalised, I was at home being attacked by all forms of demons and spirits. For two hours I fought them and started speaking in an ancient language I'd never heard before. At about five o'clock in the morning, I stopped fighting the demons and stepped outside my door to buy some milk to drink. The neighbours must have rung the police because when I went outside, they were waiting for me and called me over. I used to carry a stick at the time because I'd become like an ancient Chinese warrior because of my Chinese heritage. The police came at me and I instinctively started to do kung fu like Bruce Lee. Eventually they overpowered me, cuffed me and took me to Brixton Police Station. The doctors were called but I could tell they weren't ordinary doctors. I felt like one of them looked into my soul while the other asked me some questions. At the time I couldn't eat certain food, like fish and meat, or drink water, because I thought they stank. I could only drink milk and eat fruit, so I refused when they offered me food or water. In the police cells I heard threatening voices, like Satan sending out his people to come and get me. I was very nervous and said to the policemen, "Are you going to take me and kill me now?" They said they didn't think I was well and wanted to take me to hospital for an assessment, but I didn't realise they meant a mental hospital.

Contact with services and treatment

I was handed over to the doctors, who took me to a hospital near Baker Street that seemed like a hotel, where they assessed me. A week later, I was taken to South Western Hospital at Landor Road, Stockwell. Initially, I was in hospital for 28 days because I had signed a form saying that I agreed to treatment. But I wanted to go home, so began a legal fight with them. After 28 days, they wouldn't let me go so I was Sectioned, but eventually my mental health solicitor got a court order for me to be released. My solicitor became like my protector - I would call her whenever they wanted me to go back into hospital and she would offer me her advice.

I was having terrible side effects from the tablets they had given me and thought I was dying. I was like a zombie and found it very hard to breathe. After the first experience with the tablets, I said I wasn't going to take them any more. This young doctor said that if I didn't, they had a right to hold me down and inject me. I made it very clear I was taking no more of this medication. So I asked to see another doctor and they brought me a very nice Latin-American woman who said she would try and find me another type of medication. So she put me on olanzapine which worked OK and made me sleep a lot so my mind could rest. I could still hear a million voices in my head while I was asleep but the medication knocked me out. There weren't any side effects from this medication so when they wanted to increase the dosage, I agreed. This doctor was an innovator and inspiration, experimenting with the use of music and art therapy to bring the patients out of themselves. There was a keyboard in the hospital but nobody was playing it because all the patients were walking around like zombies. So I started to play and that's how I got into music. I'm not a trained pianist but was getting a sound out of the thing, like someone else had taken over my body. I was also singing a lot at that time and had been singing the hymn *Rock of Ages* when I was first taken to the police station. Music became therapeutic because when you're not sleeping, there's nothing else to do.

When I came out of hospital, I would last for a year and then something stressful would happen in my life so I would get the symptoms again, but more intense and traumatic. I realised that when I was getting more ill I couldn't cope by myself, so would go back into hospital again. In total I've been in voluntarily three times because I needed the support of the hospital or the caring team. The first time I was in hospital, I was diagnosed with paranoid schizophrenia. I knew what the word paranoid meant but didn't know what schizophrenia was. But they were doctors and I accepted whatever they said. I just wanted my freedom and to get out. My last hospital admission was around five years ago. After this, I was released into the community and would go and visit the psychiatrist at a community mental health team in Streatham. After three years they discharged me from the team because I was OK and they said I didn't need their support any more.

Contact with mental health professionals

Frankly mental health professionals haven't helped me very much, although I have met some very nice people along the way. As a patient you have a view and understanding of what you are going through. Trying to get them to get into your mind is a long arduous process. But I've met some very empathic people who have listened to me. The biggest help mental health professionals can be is to give a listening ear to the person who is ill. The most help I've had is when I've been able to talk about what I've been going through, they listen and say they understand, not that I'm mad. You need that person to talk to who is a professional.

The music therapy I had with the Latin-American doctor was very helpful and I felt like she was an African spirit in a Latin body. I was talking to her about Shamanism, telling her I was a bridge between the spiritual and material worlds. Hearing those sorts of terms was no big deal to her because she came from a culture where they are understood. When I said this to the English doctors they would just say, "Yes Mr Lee," but she understood me. I've met very highly intelligent doctors who knew what I was going through but she was the only person who would sit down, talk to me and try to understand me.

The main problem a lot of doctors have is that they have very little idea of the spiritual beliefs of their patients. They view your illness on a medical pathway. Lots of people with mental illness go through a spiritual experience, so it would be nice if doctors knew a little bit about religion or spirituality. That way they can understand you better. If you are dealing with people who are going through what they deem as a spiritual experience, you should have some basic idea what they are talking about. So if the patient's deity is the Nigerian God Ogun, the doctors ought to know. There are quite a lot of African people going through the mental health system and they will not accept the doctors if they can't identify with their spirituality.

I attend the Fanon Resource Centre in Brixton each week, a mental health centre for African and Caribbean people. The manageress there really connects to us because she understands us and our culture. She's also very creative and got the money for us to buy some musical equipment and pay for a music teacher. We used to have a music jam class every Friday afternoon and you could go if you were a singer or musician. I heard about it and went along, but the teacher left and the centre was taken under new management. The music was killed off due to the budget situation so I didn't go for a while because the place was dead. I told the manageress that I wasn't going back until there was music, so she got a little budget together to continue the project. There was already a keyboard there and she said I could go and buy bass and acoustic guitars. Despite being restrained by her budget, she fought tooth and nail to get us what we wanted.

People like to feel purposeful and because you're suffering from a condition it doesn't mean you become obsolete. We are always being told to go and get IT training but a lot of people like me want to do art or music. Mental health professionals should find some way of facilitating what the patients want to do. They need to balance the patient's therapy with whatever their dream or purpose is.

Transition towards recovery

You learn to cope with your condition but the first thing to deal with is the shock. You're a bright, normal person doing your job and then you have to come to an adjustment. There is a stigma about it and you don't want to share it with friends or other people. Then you are told to go to social centres where you see other people with mental health conditions. The biggest word is 'disability' – you have got to accept that you are a disabled person, like you have had your legs chopped off. Before you were a man of the world and could take on anything but all of a sudden you have got this stigma that you are disabled. The stigma can never truly be overcome. You have to find your own inner strength to overcome a bullying society. When you seek approval or acceptance, you are going about things the wrong way. Society has to accept you, but it's not an easy road to take.

A turning point for me was when I started to have a relationship with God or the Creator. I began a path search, thinking that if there was a God I was going to find Him. So I started to read books on higher consciousness to get deeper into understanding what life is about. It made me realise I had a purpose in life and that my destiny was beyond my appearance or what anybody else thought it was. My purpose and destiny is to spread love and joy to the world through art.

Frankly I never accepted that I was sick, it was the doctors that told me I was sick. As far as I was concerned, I was going through a spiritual experience and even today I don't consider myself sick. What I've been through has made me so gifted that I can see things and I wouldn't take away that experience. I just deal with a condition where I am a bridge between the spiritual and material worlds. I used to view the world through white educated eyes but I began to express my outlook from the perspective of African and Chinese philosophy. This is the person I am today and I can't be somebody else. I call it a rebirth. The person before was not the real me but it was my destiny to have my eyes opened.

Making recovery a reality

When I came out of hospital, I tried to get back into normal work and find a job. I took an Access to Music course at Morley College to fill my days. This was helpful in my recovery because instead of sitting around in the day time, I had something to do. I was writing songs and could play naturally but didn't have any musical training. I wanted to know basic music theory so I could understand what I was doing. With this course, you didn't need any training as they try and fast track you in understanding music. I learned a bit of jazz, classical and opera on the course – you could just go in and pick the piece that you were interested in. I still can't read music but when I play chords, I now know what I'm doing and can understand basic music theory. Doing the course got my mind into something so I wasn't drifting away aimlessly. It got me passionate about music and still helps me today because I write one or two songs every week.

Now I come to the Fanon Resource Centre so I have somewhere to socialise and can have a conversation with people. Here I'm among my own people, can enjoy Afro-Caribbean food and see that people like me are going through the same thing. I taught a six week Introduction to Song Writing course at the centre which got the service users to be more self-expressive and exercise their creativity. It helped them to understand that the thoughts they had in their heads weren't mad. It was also my idea to start a regular music class and a capella choir. I do this as an empowerment tool so they can start making their own music, poetry or whatever else they want to do. Music is a form of expression which brings out the inner self. If you are ill then your spirit is depressed, but music can empower it to get up again.

I used to work for London County Council's youth service and when I was there, wrote a song called The Best in Me which helped me to win a Millennium Grant worth £3,000. I used the money to run a six-week summer mentoring scheme called the Rainbow Music Project where I mentored children with musical talent from local youth clubs. The project got me into doing something where I felt useful and could help somebody. My dream is to restart the project as after school music clubs to teach children the music they want to do on an informal basis.

Hope

I understand the concept of hope but I don't accept it. Hope is a false concept - Barack Obama wrote that hope isn't real, you have to make it exist. He said that hope is wishing and isn't tangible, but could always be there one day. It's about believing in change and making it happen. More important than hope is love and the greatest love of all is learning to love yourself. To do this, you have to go through the pain of self-acceptance. You have got to find the inner strength to reject hate. When I didn't love myself there was no hope. It's your soul that sings and it doesn't need a licence to be free. I used to believe in hope or charity but faith is what has brought me through. Hope is wishing someone will hold your hand but I believe in empowerment. What you do in a small way is what you can learn to do in a big way. Making the first step is what's important. Do good and good will beget good.

Reflection

After a long search, I believe the reason that most black people are going through psychosis is because of what I deem as 'slavery trauma'. This is where the trauma of slavery has remained in our DNA throughout the generations. There comes a point when the souls of our spiritual ancestors connect to us and this is a very powerful force. What mentally ill people think are demons and devils are actually the voices of our ancestors trying to claim us back.

There is often a conflict of interest in the treatment of black people with mental illness. I don't know why the English white medical establishment cannot accept slavery trauma because many of their patients are black. The doctors know about the black experience of psychosis but there is a white Western denial about slavery trauma. They are just paying lip service when there are many eminent black doctors who have written about it, such as the psychiatrist Frantz Fanon. When the doctors start to accept slavery trauma as part of psychosis, things will improve for black people with mental illness. But I can't take on the whole medical establishment myself.

Conclusion

Other people can look at me and see they can conquer their fear or hate or whatever their demons are. Recovery is having the inner strength to conquer your demons. They mustn't rule you because you need a relationship with them. Knowing what you stand for in life and your purpose can help you to conquer fear.

Forging His Own Path

Chapter 14

Forging His Own Path

Peter Bullimore, 48, from Sheffield, was a successful businessman and married father of three who lost everything during many years of psychosis. He has now recovered and works as a consultant for the Hearing Voices Network, delivering training and teaching on hearing voices and paranoia all over the world.

Background

I believe my psychosis started through childhood sexual abuse. The babysitter would come round on a Friday evening and put on a horror programme called *Appointment with Fear*. I was quite a nervous child and didn't want to watch it, but she would make me. She'd turn the lights out so it was dark and keep giving me glasses of pop. Eventually I'd say I wanted to go to the loo but would be too frightened to go upstairs, so would wet myself. When my parents came home, the television was off and the lights were on and she'd say, "I told him to go to the toilet but he took no notice". At such a young age I thought if they believed that, they would believe anything. That's when the abuse really started. It was sexual, physical and downright disgusting. This went on from the age of five until I was nearly 13 but I was too frightened to tell anybody.

When I got to seven I became very paranoid, thinking the entire world knew what was happening but no one was prepared to help me. So I became very socially isolated and started to hear voices. As I got older the abuse escalated, getting more intense and severe. When I was being abused at the age of 12, there were times that I would get aroused, but just couldn't understand why because I hated it. When that happened, the voices would return to criticise me. One voice became ten, ten voices became 20, and they were very destructive and violent. I was carrying this secret around that I just couldn't tell anyone and it really affected my behaviour. It got to the point where I hit my best friend because I thought my head was going to explode. We had an electric lawnmower and one day my mum was cleaning the blades. The voices urged me to turn it on, which I did and nearly cut her fingers off.

The lowest point turned out to be a turning point on reflection. Just before my thirteenth birthday, the babysitter came round and had full sex with me. I was so worried she could be pregnant. Eventually I said to my parents that I didn't want this woman coming round anymore and they agreed. The abuse stopped and the voices went away, lying repressed and buried until the age of about 19.

Transition towards illness

The problem was I never told anyone about the voices or the abuse. I got married at a young age and became a father but I never told my wife what I was going through. It was during the recession and I'd lost my job but couldn't find work. We had three children, the house was threatened with repossession and I had no idea how we were going to survive. Eventually I found work manufacturing fire surrounds. This was a good job but I was working seven days a week and not making any impression on the money we owed. Under these stresses and pressures, the voices came back. I can remember the first one. It was a Friday evening, I'd just got paid and was walking into Sheffield town centre when I was hit by a really loud, dominant voice. It kept saying, "You are Mickey McAvoy, you're worth millions!" He's the bloke that robbed the Brink's Mat gold in London and I foolishly believed what this voice was telling me. So I walked into the first pub I found and bought everybody a drink, then another. When I went home I was in real trouble as I'd got no money left. But I couldn't explain why I'd done it and my wife thought I was crazy.

Realisation of a problem

For a period of months things ebbed and flowed. The voices would be there then go away. A friend of mine asked if I would like to go into business with him. So we set up a business manufacturing fire surrounds and in the first year it turned over a million pounds. But it became a monster - we were working 18 hours a day, seven days a week. Unbeknown to my wife, she became my tormenter. She loved the lifestyle she'd got now – massive house, car and everything she wanted - but she wanted me at home as well. So I felt really trapped, like the babysitter was abusing my mind again, and my behaviour started to spiral out of control. On one occasion, a white car followed me for two or three streets, and I turned the works van across the road so it couldn't get past. I jumped out and banged on their windows asking them why they were following me. You can imagine their reaction. Then I was driving home late one night and turned down this country lane. I looked in the mirror and could see this Freddy Krueger character from the

Nightmare on Elm Street films in the back of the van. So I pulled over and jumped out, throwing everything in the van out into the road. Cars couldn't get past and were blasting their horns to get me to move but I was shouting, "F – off, I'm looking for Freddy Krueger."

Crisis point

I had nowhere to turn and it was a living hell. My wife encouraged me to see a doctor who just said I was stressed and gave me beta blockers. But I had a really bad period of insomnia and hadn't slept properly for days. It was the early hours of Sunday morning and I was lying on the settee on the front room when I had an out of body experience. I couldn't get back into my body and thought I was dead. Eventually I started to cry uncontrollably which is something I'd learnt as a child you don't do, as it's a sign of weakness. My wife kept asking me what was wrong and I said to her, "Why did you let me die on my own, after all I've done for you?" She couldn't understand what I was saying and encouraged me not to go to work the next day. But I ignored her and went. There was a problem on a job and this man was shouting down the phone at me so I told him to f– off. My business partner said, "You can't speak to people like that!" which was the final straw, so I hit him over the head with the telephone and walked out. I went home and just curled up in a chair. I didn't wash, I didn't shave and I didn't eat or drink properly - I was just locked in this fearful world of voices, paranoia and depression.

Contact with services and treatment

Eventually the doctor came and said he thought I should go into hospital. At this time I was very ignorant about mental health so I thought they'd put me on a general ward with nurses fussing round for a few weeks. But that night my dad drove me to the local psychiatric unit. The experience was a real eye opener. It was horrible. The hospital was absolutely filthy, there were double mattresses on single beds and people lying in the corridors. Eventually a doctor came to see me and said she was going to give me a rectal examination. I've no idea why this was necessary, but it was like the abuse all over again and part of the paranoid plot. I ran down the corridor and was stopped by this male nurse who said if I tried to leave, they would Section me. I realise now that is coercion and is actually illegal. But not knowing that at the time, I stayed and was Sectioned for the first of many times over ten years. During this first admission, I couldn't look in the mirror because I couldn't see myself, only a demon. The figure had long hair, a beard and was black round the eyes. On reflection, that was me! I was taking a combination of 25 drugs a day so had gone black round the eyes.

But the voices were still there. About six months later, I asked my worker if I could go home. He told me to sit at the end of the ward and wait for the doctor. I sat there from nine o'clock in the morning to six o'clock at night but when I asked when I would see the doctor, they said he'd forgotten about me. The following week exactly the same thing happened. So I learned the golden rule of getting out of a psychiatric unit – tell lies. I managed to get out and as I was leaving my wife and parents asked the staff what was wrong with me. But they said it was confidential so they should ask me. Well I couldn't explain anything to them as no one had explained anything to me. I'd been diagnosed when I first went into the mental health system and remember the consultant psychiatrist's words, "Mr Bullimore, you are a chronic schizophrenic and you will never, ever work again. Go away and enjoy your life." But he never told me what schizophrenia was. Personally I don't believe schizophrenia even exists and I had to get rid of the diagnosis before recovery was possible.

So I went home but used to have night terrors which were very frightening. One evening my wife had turned the light off and I jumped up screaming. She tried to comfort me but I couldn't see her, only what had been in this night terror. I jumped on her and started to strangle her. Fortunately she threw me off and went and locked herself in the front room downstairs leaving me with three young children upstairs in a very disturbed state. So I got re-Sectioned and given so many drugs I couldn't bend my arms, like I was pushing an invisible wheelbarrow around the ward. One day I came back from breakfast and there was a man in my bed. I told the nursing staff but they said there was nothing they could do as there were 32 patients and 29 beds. I needed to lie down so I wandered off the ward and found the administration block where there was a big disabled toilet. I went in there, took my jumper off and slept on the toilet floor. This went on for two weeks because there was no bed for me during the day.

When I was released, I moved into a flat for the mentally ill in Sheffield having separated from my wife. But it was unfurnished so I was back to sleeping on the floor again. Luckily one of the neighbours rang the Council which helped me get a grant for £650 from the mental health Citizen's Advice Bureau. I started to attend a day centre and moved in with my parents for a while. Family carers are worth a million pounds a week, but they are also great at getting it wrong. I was a grown man with three kids and my mum had started tucking me into bed again!

I was still very paranoid and went through a kind of emotional shutdown. I couldn't cope and took my first overdose but fortunately woke up covered in vomit. Then I had a really bad visual hallucination of two monks standing at the bottom of my bed. One was pointing at me and the other one walked straight through the bed and into me. I was convinced I was possessed by this monk and he was eating my food. In a month I'd lost a stone in weight so I told my worker at the centre. He sent me to have cameras pushed in every orifice so it felt like I was being abused again. I just thought, do these so-called intelligent people not realise that rapid weight loss can be a sign of psychosis?

Contact with mental health professionals

Then I got a new occupational therapist who was amazing. She never, ever treated my diagnosis but always looked beyond it to me. When you're in the mental health system you tend to put everyone on a pedestal as your confidence and self-esteem are so low. She addressed that by telling me a bit about herself and the stresses and traumas she'd had in her life. I thought, wow, this woman does understand and has got feelings and emotions. She asked me why I isolated myself on a Friday and found out that was the day I was abused. I couldn't cope but she helped me work through it. I also got a new psychiatrist who was great – young and enthusiastic. He wasn't bothered about an appointment system and had an "open door policy" which I really liked. He started to reduce my drugs to 2,400mg of sulpiride a day, so things were picking up.

A social worker told me about a support group for people who hear voices run by Sheffield Mind and encouraged me to go. At this point I was the archetypal schizophrenic - I didn't wash or shave and was scruffy. There were ten other people at this group but it struck me that they were all smart and presentable. I thought they couldn't be "schizos" as they would be scruffy like me! But when they started to share their experiences I realised that was where I belonged and could take the mask off that I'd been wearing for years. They asked me if I wanted to go to a workshop but I didn't know what a workshop was. So I turned up thinking, where's the workbench, what are we going to make? But three people from the Hearing Voices Network shared their experiences of recovery and what really struck me was the content of their voices was related to life events. I suddenly thought that perhaps there was another explanation for all this. I was still on nearly every medication, but the seed of doubt had been sown by the Hearing Voices Network speakers.

Foolishly I then tried to evaluate my life. I stopped going to the group, but didn't realise how much support I was losing. I stopped listening to the occupational therapist and the psychiatrist but I was very fortunate they didn't give up on me. The delusions started to return. I'd had an out of body experience, died and been resurrected, and been to hell and back on the acute ward. So it fitted that I must be Jesus Christ! I always say you're not a fully paid up member of the psychotic's society unless you've been Jesus.

I thought about what to do with this new found information, so I went to Sheffield Cathedral to show myself. There was a pulpit facing the main auditorium where a vicar was doing a sermon to some old age pensioners. So I seized my chance and jumped in the pulpit beside him. He turned around and said, "Christ Almighty!" and I thought, "Brilliant, he actually recognises me!" He stopped the sermon and took me to a back room, where he asked me if I'd ever been in a mental hospital. He said he was starting a group for people with mental health problems, but unfortunately I never heard from him again.

The psychiatrist said he was going to give me a chance and cut the drugs by 50 per cent to see how I'd function. It actually felt fantastic - I could start to feel my limbs again. But it occurred to me it was my destiny to kill myself, so I went to tell my psychiatrist. When you've been on medication for years, you forget words so I said to him, "I was born to kill..." You've never seen somebody's chair move back as fast in your life. So he doubled my medication, Sectioned me and went to work in another Trust! I've got respect for him as he did a lot for me but I've seen both ends of the scale. When I was re-Sectioned I met another psychiatrist who was an absolute nightmare. For some reason she just hated me. I thought if I looked at her she'd put my drugs up, or if I smiled at her I'd be on Lithium on top of everything else. I was so heavily medicated I used to just lie on my bed all day. My parents used to have to bring in tea towels as bibs to mop up the slime that had dribbled out of my mouth. The psychiatrist told me she wouldn't let me out unless I started speaking to people. So I started telling the nurse what the voices said, but then the psychiatrist said she couldn't let me out because I was too delusional!

Transition towards recovery

Eventually I managed to lie my way out but the voices were by now relentless. They convinced me that I'd killed my mother, who had died from cancer six months earlier. I tried to set myself alight and then slashed my wrists. When I was recovering from the second suicide attempt my dad came to visit. It proved to be a turning point in my life because he asked me why I'd done it. He said, "I've just lost your mum, I don't want to lose you too." It was the look of utter despair in his face that made me realise I had to stop being selfish and I was hurting other people, not just myself. My mum and dad, the occupational therapist and psychiatrist had done everything they could. The only person who wasn't trying was me. The reason for this was that ten years earlier a consultant psychiatrist had said I would never, ever work again. That's how powerful his words had been.

When I got released, my divorce came through and I fell into a relationship with a younger woman. One night she got drunk and smashed a vase into my face, leaving me with 19 stitches. Even though there were nine witnesses, it was me who got hauled in by the police because I was a known schizophrenic. This got to Crown Court and she was found guilty. As I was coming out of court, my occupational therapist asked me how I was and how were the voices. I told her they were there, but not too aggressive. She said I had just turned a corner in my life, as normally I would have ended up in hospital under that amount of stress. I had to build on this but didn't know what to do. She told me that the hearing voices group at Mind had closed and suggested I started another one. So together we set up a hearing voices support and education group which is now the longest-running in the country with 85 members. I also tracked down the Hearing Voices Network, where somebody recommended a book called *Accepting Voices* by Marius Romme and Sandra Escher (1993), the most inspiring book I'd ever read about hearing voices. I invited the Hearing Voices Network to Sheffield and was talking to the course facilitator, who knew I was a voice hearer. I said the voices he'd spoken about had an identity, whereas mine were just demonic. He looked me straight in the eye and said, "Peter, address the demons of your past." The demon of my past was my abuser and as a grown man I still used to run away when I saw her. One Saturday afternoon she was coming down the road towards me and my first instinct was to run. But I didn't, I kept walking towards her and looked her full in the face. She just kept looking at the floor and I realised she didn't have power over me anymore.

The mental health system disempowers people and I realised I needed to take the power back for myself. So I locked myself away and listened intently to what the voices were telling me. I discovered they were trying to be helpful, not nasty, by telling me I hadn't dealt with the layers of guilt, confusion, anger and pleasure relating to my abuse. The guilt was the worst for me, because some of the abuse was pleasurable. But I had to let that go, so I put myself on trial in a court of law in my mind. The fact was I had been a child at the time and had no choice. So I found myself innocent of all charges and could let the guilt go.

Making recovery a reality

From then on my recovery was very quick. I got more involved with the Hearing Voices Network, started my own training and consultancy business called Asylum Associates and set up the Paranoia Network which all helped. I still hear voices all day every day but they're not as powerful any more and I don't take any medication. Psychiatry would say I'm not recovered as I still hear voices, but I think that's a very dangerous view. It's a good thing when my voices get loud because they are my early warning signs. They are saying I've done too much and when they increase in negativity I know I've got to slow down. Getting rid of voices has become the Holy Grail but I think the answer is to have a relationship with them and understand why they are there.

In my current job as a training consultant for the Hearing Voices Network, I try to get psychiatrists to look at different strategies for working with voices. I personally don't believe that when the voices start, they should go in with big doses of medication. These block the person's cognition so they can't interact. They should try and get the person to interact and if they don't, give them a small amount just to take the edge off. I also think they need to ask the right questions when people enter acute services, like how they came to be there or what was happening in their life. People don't get up one day and decide to be mad. Something brings you to those circumstances and psychiatrists have got to ask the right questions to find out.

Hope

People say my story has given them great hope that you can go through a lot of adversity in your life and survive. Hope is massively important and I've been given it by the people around me, including my children. Hopefully people will learn from the mistakes I made, such as disengaging from the hearing voices group and trying to push the psychiatrist and occupational therapist away. You have to use the resources around you and not try and get through it alone. When I was living on the streets for a while I became hopeless. I was sleeping under a stairwell and at three o'clock in the morning this gang of lads came back from a night out and urinated all over me. I just thought I couldn't get any lower but the hope began to come back when I met other people with psychosis. I hope to continue working to spread the word and foster hope for people like us. But I know I can't keep on doing it forever so my main hope is to eventually become a children's author.

Reflection

Before I had psychosis, I was like a lost child but it helped me discover who I really am and who I want to be. The experience has made me a better person. When I had the business, I didn't like myself and money had become my God. But I like myself now, I've got an amazing relationship with my children and I feel more content than ever. I wake up each day and look forward to work because I can help people on the same journey. I've also got a positive voice now which I've never had before. It woke me up a few months ago with an idea for a children's book. It's released my creativity and I can't start a chapter until the voice tells me what to write about.

Conclusion

Hearing voices is a common human experience which needs to be normalised, not pathologised. If we pathologise it then we miss the person and start to treat a label rather than an individual. Labels are for bottles and cans, not people. People with psychosis also need to stop labelling themselves. I've had so many people walk up to me at conferences and say, "Hi, I'm a schizophrenic" but I say to them, "Would you come up to me and say, 'Hi, I'm a diabetic?'" We need to get rid of the whole diagnostic procedure and treat people as people.

Reference

Romme M and Escher S (eds) (1993) *Accepting Voices*. Mind: London.

A Blessing in Disguise

Chapter 15

A Blessing in Disguise

Esther Maxwell-Orumbie, 57, from Tulse Hill, South London, is an artist who developed psychosis in her late 30s. She has been treated for 20 years but is now in recovery due to her strong Christian faith and a positive outlook on life.

Background

I was born in Birkenhead and grew up partly in England and partly in Freetown, Sierra Leone, where my mother comes from. My father was from Nigeria. I've been shuffling backwards and forwards between England, Africa and the United States for much of my life. My father was an engineer and came to the UK to study and my mum was a journalist who travelled a lot for work. They divorced when I was four and I spent a lot of time with my grandparents in Freetown. When I was five we returned to Sierra Leone for a couple of years before coming back to England. After secondary school I moved to the US – first Pittsburgh then New York - because my family was there. In the US I started to study for a degree in Fine Art but dropped out because I found it too much. After another six months I headed back to Freetown where I worked as an assistant in the university library for a year and had my son. I worked in three secondary schools as a librarian. One job involved cataloguing lots of brand new books that had been donated by UNESCO and making them available to pupils. I enjoyed the work and mingling with the students. In 1977, I went to live in Nigeria with my family because my mother was working at the Festival of African Arts and Culture. We were living in Jos in Northern Nigeria and hit very hard times. Six members of my family had to survive on the living I was making from selling my art work. I was making drawings which would then be printed up as greeting cards and large pictures. Some of my work was bought by the university and a hotel, but we struggled and it was very difficult. After a year, the family decided that we shouldn't be suffering in another country so we packed our bags and returned to Sierra Leone. At that time it was easy to find a job, but the country's currency became drastically devalued and in 1985 we decided to head back to the US. I stayed in Philadelphia for a year, but couldn't find a job because I didn't have the right visa. So it was decided that because I was born in England, I should come here with my son and see what I could make of myself. I settled with an aunt-in-law in Stockwell but it was hard going because I didn't have any money. I'm a Christian and was attending a church in Oval that helped me to get my son into school. My aunt asked me to move out so I had nowhere to go, but somebody in the church agreed to let me live with them. I lived there for a year and they helped me to get benefits, but I had to move again to have an operation. As God would have it I got a council flat in Tulse Hill in 1988 and have lived there ever since. Throughout this whole time, my mental health was all right. When I eventually got ill with psychosis at the age of 37, I was told it had come at a late stage in my life. Normally people get sick with schizophrenia in their teens and twenties.

Transition towards illness

In 1989 I started studying for a BEd degree at London South Bank University with a view to becoming a primary school teacher. I enjoyed the course and did well but after two years became ill. I started seeing things and to feel things on my body. I could smell something horrible and my thinking was not quite right. I was aware that something was wrong with me but didn't know what it was, because I hadn't been mentally ill before. Then in 1991 I was in church at Easter when everything started to look strange - I could see a black halo around everyone's heads. I wasn't feeling so good physically either and wondered what on earth was going on. For about a week I struggled on, sometimes bumping myself into a wall or lamp post to make sure I wasn't dreaming.

Realisation of problem

Somehow I knew I had to go to the outpatients department of the Maudsley Hospital. I told them that something was wrong with me and asked them to help. The doctors there assessed me as an outpatient and gave me some tablets. I'd started to become paranoid so didn't take the tablets as I was afraid they would do something bad to me. I muddled along for about four years without any more contact with mental health services. All that time I was unwell and my family put up with me. In 2004, my mum said she she'd hidden all the knives and sharp objects in the flat because she was afraid I would do something drastic. She was so worried about me that one day she locked me inside our flat because I was behaving erratically. I took this long thick cord which we used to tie the curtains and hung it out of the window so I could shimmy down from the balcony. When my mum saw me hanging out of the window, she asked me what I was doing and got my sister to take me back to the Maudsley.

Crisis points

By now I was not only paranoid but terrified of what was happening to me. The doctors assessed me and decided I had to go into hospital. But I was too scared and refused, so they Sectioned me. I wouldn't get into the ambulance and they had to force me. At first I was taken to the Royal Masonic Hospital in Ravenscourt Park because there was no room at the Maudsley. They had to frogmarch me in because I refused to go of my own accord. I was in there for about ten days and was just petrified during the whole time. All the nurses wore black and I thought the hospital had something to do with Freemasonry because of its name. Finally I was transferred to the Maudsley where I remained for 28 days. This was less terrifying, but there was one nurse there who scared me. I was afraid he would come into my room at night and rape me. Initially I was put on a high dose of trifluoperazine (Stelazine) and have been on this medication ever since. A lot of people with a mental health problem are changed from tablet to tablet but I never have because the doctors found the right one for me straightaway. To begin with, it made my mouth very dry and I was very drowsy, half falling asleep all the time. Now I don't have that problem because I've got used to it. While in the Maudsley, I was diagnosed as having paranoid schizophrenia but I didn't know what that was. They told me I had a chemical imbalance in the brain which really got my back up. The diagnosis of schizophrenia was less of a problem for me than being told this. I just didn't like it and found it difficult to accept the implication that I had a malfunction in my brain.

At first I didn't know why I had become ill, but later on thought that it may have been triggered by the stress of my BEd degree studies. On both of the degree courses I began, it was the amount of work rather than the content that was too stressful for me. The medication helped me to improve gradually. Someone in my treatment team sent me to Ability, a work project for people with mental health problems and learning difficulties which is now called First Step Trust. There I attended the art department and enjoyed doing silk screen printing and drawing. They wanted an office manager so one of the tutors suggested I apply for the job. Even though I was not a hundred per cent well, I competed for the job on a national scale. Believe it or not, they said I was the best and I got the job. I worked there for about three years but it was a very stressful time for me and I didn't enjoy it. I had a lot of work to do and was struggling, though I didn't tell anybody at work. Many times I would go home and threaten to quit but my family would say, "How are you going to pay your rent or bills? You can't survive if you don't have a job." After about two years in the job I became the arts and crafts manager which I enjoyed. This involved managing about ten service users in making things to sell, like printed mugs, mosaics, greetings cards and printed t-shirts.

Contact with services and treatment

In 2000, a new service in Lambeth was created for treating people with mental illness called Lambeth Early Onset (LEO). It consisted of a ward in Lambeth Hospital and a community team. The person who was going to be the manager asked if I would like to come and work for the community team as a support worker. I applied and got the job, and worked there for seven years. My role involved doing a somewhat scaled down version of what the community psychiatric nurses did and with less responsibility. I helped service users with whatever needed to be done, such as finding them somewhere to live or a job, and accompanying them shopping or to the doctor. I also helped run a drop-in centre which gave the clients somewhere to go once a week during the evening. Some people have said to me they don't understand how I could have done that job but I loved it and didn't find it stressful at all. While I was in the workplace, I listened to all sorts of problems and issues that my clients had. But the minute I stepped outside, I dropped them and didn't take anything home with me. I was always happy to help the clients and was empathetic but never got emotionally involved. I think being able to do this was a gift. There was another lady working there who did take it home with her and found it stressful because she *did* become emotionally involved.

But in 2003 I had a major relapse while working for LEO, so much so that I handed in my resignation without consulting my family or boss. When I did this, my boss immediately knew something wasn't right because it had just come out of the blue. Luckily he rejected my resignation. All my symptoms came back and I was really in a very bad way. My family had gone away for the weekend and my flat became unbearable. I thought it had started to smell of sulphur, so couldn't stay inside and slept on the balcony at night. I was so paranoid people would come and get me I got up in the middle of the night and walked all the way from Tulse Hill to Victoria. When I got there I sat on the steps of some flats having hallucinations and hearing voices. After some time I walked back to my flat, but the voices told me to step out into the middle of the road in front of the cars speeding by. Just before the cars got to me, the voices would tell me to get back onto the kerb. This happened several times until somebody must have seen me and called the police. It was about three o'clock in the morning when they came and must have been obvious I wasn't all there from the way I was behaving. They bundled me into the police van, took me to hospital and I ended up in the Bethlem Royal Hospital for about five weeks. My paranoia persisted and I thought there was a girl there who was out to get me. But I began to use a strategy to stop myself from feeling this way. Any time the girl would come past me, I would tell myself not to look at her or think about her. This would help me and gradually the paranoia would lessen until it vanished.

I was getting better so they moved me to another ward which was a step towards getting out. In the meantime I had developed this thing about not being able to drink tap water or eat ordinary food because I thought it brought my symptoms back. I don't know whether this was real or an illusion. My cheeks were sunken and I looked as skinny as a rake, but I was afraid to eat the hospital food. There was no other food available so I forced myself to eat something. One of the doctors said I was doing well, so eventually I went home and back to work on a part time basis. Some of the symptoms I had like paranoia persisted. In 2005 I relapsed again but didn't go into hospital because I didn't tell anybody I was ill apart from my family. They suggested I go and see a doctor but I struggled along with a high degree of paranoia on my own. I even had delusions about my son being the Devil which was very difficult because I love him very much. I never told him what I was thinking and at times we would get angry with each other, then I'd feel guilty. This mental battle was going on but I resolved it by thinking to myself that I didn't have the spiritual capacity to know whether my son was the Devil or not. I just had to believe that he was my son and to be good to him. This way I managed to work my way through the paranoia again, the symptoms disappeared and I became well again.

There were periods when I would toy with my medication. When this happened, I would relapse with voices, paranoia, seeing things and feeling things on my body. Out on the streets I would think that people were out to attack me and do me harm. I would try and tune out the voices but this can be difficult when they are in your head. There were certain buses I wouldn't use because I thought the people on them were out to get me. There was a time when I walked from Tulse Hill to Notting Hill Gate because I was scared that people would harm me if I got the bus. During a relapse in 2007, I impulsively handed in my resignation because I couldn't cope with the pressure of working and dealing with my mental health situation. I quit without telling either my psychologist or psychiatrist, but my psychologist said I should have told him so he could have negotiated for me to go back into work gradually. I haven't worked since that point and have been concentrating on my art work. This includes making appliqué wall hangings, prints and greeting cards which I sell. At the moment I am well, unless I reduce my medication. I'm not paranoid or hearing voices and am concentrating on life outside my illness.

Contact with mental health professionals

The psychiatrist who treated me in the Maudsley was the best mental health professional I have encountered. I've always argued with my doctors but I never argued with him because he seemed to understand me and listened. Another doctor I had supported me if I wanted to reduce my medication.

She had a listening ear and didn't seem narrow minded. There was one psychiatrist who I used to argue with a lot because all that mattered to him was that I took my medication. I agree with taking medication but only to a certain point. Maybe he knew his subject matter, but he didn't know how to put it across. He was not a very warm, caring person. My present psychologist is tremendous, not only by being very concerned about my mental wellbeing but also in my life outside of the illness. He has gone the extra mile in trying to promote my artwork and has also purchased a lot of my work.

Lots of mental health professionals don't believe in God, but they also think that you shouldn't believe in God either. They think it sets you back and makes you worse which I think is very wrong. But when it comes to religion, they should leave people alone and keep their thoughts to themselves. Spirituality is something that helps people. Professionals could have recognised my Christian beliefs, but if I was a Buddhist they should respect that too. I'm not just a lump of flesh, I am a spirit inside a body and my spiritual dimension must be recognised. I want to see professionals listen to and accept the role of spirituality in people's lives, not knock it. If they don't like it they should keep their mouths shut.

Professionals should have a listening ear to what the service user has to say and put into practise some of the methods they want used. For example, if the service user wants to try a certain therapy the professional should help them to give it a go. They need to understand that we are human beings with feelings. Being an empathetic and caring professional is also important, although difficult if they have never suffered from mental illness or psychosis themselves. When I worked at LEO the service users sometimes preferred to talk to us rather than the doctors and nurses. I've been in a meeting where a service user has gone berserk because the doctor was too clinical and not human enough.

Transition towards recovery

Compared to a few years ago I am in recovery but before that I was muddling along. I've been ill for 20 years but nobody told me recovery was possible until I started working with my psychologist. Before this, all I knew was to take my medication and get on with it. Now I attend the recovery groups that are run by my psychologist, where I am learning that recovery is possible. I know I am on the road to recovery because my insight is still intact. If I begin to get some symptoms I know what I should be doing, such as slowing down, taking things easy and making sure I'm on the right dose of medication. Recovery for me is coming off benefits, getting a job and living a normal life. Being mentally ill is totally abnormal for me because I am not in the state which God made me.

Making recovery a reality

My belief in God has helped me a great deal in my recovery journey. When I got ill, I wasn't living the life I should as a Christian and was compromising in certain areas. I was living a double life and this was part of the reason for my mental breakdown. It made me look at my Christian life and get my act together. So in a way this illness has been a blessing in disguise because it's made me become more dedicated to the Lord. I am now more focused in my Christian life and don't compromise any more. I know that many people don't believe in God and that's the way life is, but I do believe and this has kept me going. Apart from the medication this is what has kept me well. Without my Christian faith I don't know what I would have done because it has given me an anchor. People actually say that they can feel the peace around me. God is my heavenly father and I know He loves me dearly, cares for me and wants the best for me. I think my story could inspire anyone who believes in God, because my faith has helped me. If they are a Christian too, they can look at my journey and have their faith revitalised. Those that don't believe in God could be encouraged by the fact that I have some insight, am able to rethink my thoughts and try and help myself in order to overcome obstacles.

Fear can be a hindrance to recovery. Sometimes I'm unwilling to step forward and try something new, such as eating certain food and drink. Now I'm being braver and even bought some fish the other day which I would never normally do. Thinking differently is helping me to move in the right direction and be determined. For example, when I go to church I don't take communion because my heart starts to palpitate like I'm getting a panic attack. Last Sunday I decided to go up and take communion no matter what, even if my heart started to palpitate. So I partook and went and sat down in another part of the church to calm down. This determination to overcome the symptoms helps me even though they sometimes persist. Feel the fear and do it anyway! Being able to function in an ordinary environment without being overcome by your illness is recovery.

Hope

Hope is fantastic in helping with recovery. When I was a teenager living in the US I used to get panic attacks because it was such a culture shock for me. Sometimes thoughts of suicide would come into my mind but I would reject them. I always knew that however long the road was, there would always be something good further along. This positive outlook has helped me with my recovery. I always know tomorrow will be a good day and the sun is going to shine. If I don't see good today I will see it tomorrow.

When I first got my flat I was feeling confused and we had no money to get anything to eat. That was the only time in my life I felt hopeless and it was the most horrible feeling ever. It was then that I understood why people commit suicide. Apart from this period I've always had a measure of hope in my life. I just know that life is good even though I have lots of ups and downs.

I would hope to come off my medication eventually and be completely well. I believe that as long as I am on medication I am unwell. This is silly because I could have diabetes and would need to take medication for that. But because there is so much stigma surrounding mental illness I feel I have to be off medication to be a hundred per cent well.

Reflection

Psychosis has shown me to take life very slowly and to take my faith seriously. I now take God at His word and stand firm in my Christian roots. It's also taught me to have integrity and enjoy the moment because you never know if it's going to be taken away or you're going to end up in hospital. I've been so desperate and distraught at points in my journey, that I realise you have to make the best of what you have.

Cooperating with your doctor is important and don't be afraid to tell them what's on your mind, because they're not psychic. Keep in touch with your social network and don't be isolated. Enjoy life and be good to other people. Learn to face your negative experiences full on as best you can and don't be afraid of them.

Conclusion

I am happy and content. I'm not living in the lap of luxury but I'm satisfied with what I have. Yes I have a mental health problem but it's not the end of the world. My family has been very, very supportive throughout my illness. I thank God for the family He has put me in, and I am very grateful for all the support and help that I have received from them. Before I got ill I wasn't living as I should. Now I take the opportunities that are offered to me because with psychosis, I just don't know when they are going to come my way again. Life is a serious business but I don't take myself too seriously. I grab the moment and enjoy it.

A Positive Perspective on Psychosis

Photo: Jane Fradgley

Chapter 16

A Positive Perspective on Psychosis

Peter Chadwick, 64, from Norwich, experienced psychosis after experimenting with transvestism in his twenties. This caused him to develop paranoia but he recovered and went onto have a successful career as a psychology lecturer. He has written over a hundred articles and five books, including many which highlight the positive aspects of psychosis.

Background

I was born in Manchester and brought up in a very macho, Northern way. My mother encouraged me to be a hard case which I didn't like because I knew it wasn't really me. I'd always been discriminated against for not being a regular guy. At school, the football team thought I was homosexual because I had a Cliff Richard-style hairdo. By my late twenties I was determined to explore my feminine side through becoming a transvestite. It felt this was more like my real personality than the role I'd been given growing up. You wouldn't believe it to look at me now but I made a very convincing woman. Experimenting with my gender and sexuality through transvestism did me a lot of good. Before that time I was pursuing an academic career in Geology and obtained a BSc from University College of Wales, Aberystwyth and an MSc from Imperial College, London. After getting my PhD from Liverpool University I went to Uppsala in Sweden to take up a Royal Society European Programme research post. When I came back, I decided to switch my attention to the study of psychology. Changing to psychology fed into the research I'd been doing on psychological factors in earth science such as observation and memory problems. So I went to do a BSc in psychology at the University of Bristol, which is where my transvestism really blossomed but where I was first 'outed' by the neighbours.

Transition towards illness

In those days, I felt very guilty and ashamed about being a transvestite. As the years went by I started to get increasingly paranoid that people knew what I was when I ventured out in public. I was working as a psychology lecturer at the University of Strathclyde but Glasgow wasn't the place for a transvestite. I didn't feel happy, so I left and moved to London. My paranoia developed into delusions and I started to interpret what I was doing – a man behaving as a woman - in a Satanic way. At one point I believed that the sensuous, sybaritic side to my personality was due to possession by Satan. Things started to go seriously wrong and in September 1979 I threw myself under the wheels of a double decker bus on the New King's Road in Fulham. I'd interpreted New King's Road as "the road of the New King" where Jesus would come into the world and Satan would be cast out. I reasoned that when the wheel of the bus went over my head, Satan would be thrust out of my mind and Jesus would come into the world to reign. So I had to sacrifice myself. After the suicide attempt, I was taken into hospital where they realised I was psychotic and gave me medication. This was my only major psychotic episode apart from a hiccup the previous summer, when I had experienced hallucinations and voices in my head. I thought people in the flat next door were talking about me and I could hear them through the walls. Eventually these thoughts developed into voices. I went to stay in a caravan with my girlfriend and we played Radio 1 so loudly I couldn't hear them and after a week they were gone. I think this episode was also caused by the guilt and shame of being a transvestite. After the suicide attempt, I returned to transvestism but wasn't really into it, because I still felt so guilty and ashamed of what I was doing. I'd been dressing up almost every day - going to clubs and restaurants - whereas most people only do it once a week. Within a year I'd almost burnt myself out with transvestism and pretty well stopped completely by the time I was 34.

Crisis points

I was injured from the suicide attempt – the bus missed my head but crushed my hand – so I remained in Charing Cross Hospital for a few weeks while this was seen to. I first met my wife Jill in hospital, who was being treated for a bout of depression. Meeting Jill was a turning point and we started going out together a year later. She was perfectly accepting of what had happened to me having had mental health problems herself, and we were both taking medication. When I was discharged, I was on the drug pimozide but it wasn't right for me so the doctors tried other medication including haloperidol. But they gave me too much and I experienced side effects including staring eyes and a greasy skin. Eventually a psychiatrist gave me a lower dose of haloperidol and that was when I really started to feel better. It was remarkably effective and bounced me out of the episode very well. I still take a 0.5 milligram tablet every day and as long as I do, am perfectly all right. On leaving Charing Cross Hospital I was placed into a psychiatric aftercare hostel in Shepherd's Bush for 18 months where I was seen by social workers. Jill and I managed to get a flat together and have now been married for 27 years. I was working again as a lecturer by February 1982, first for the Open

University and then for Birkbeck College, part of the University of London. This combination of a relationship, a job, good accommodation and a bit of money really helped to launch me back into my life.

Contact with services and treatment

My diagnosis has varied over the years, from atypical hypomania to schizoaffective disorder. The delusional ideas I was having made the illness more than a mood disorder, so schizoaffective disorder is probably the right diagnosis. My undergraduate psychology training was very anti-psychiatry so I didn't know much about schizophrenia, apart from that symptoms included hearing voices. The university had taught me about the ideas of the psychiatrist RD Laing, who believed that mental health problems are an understandable reaction to an unbearable social situation, and Thomas Szasz, who didn't believe mental illness existed at all. Reading their work made me miss the tell-tale signs of my approaching illness when my delusions began to pick up momentum. Consequently I underrated how serious the illness was and thought it was just a normal perceptual thing.

Contact with mental health professionals

There was very little interest in the whys and wherefores of my suicide attempt from the mental health professionals who treated me. The philosophy that they had in hospital was that schizophrenia, hypomania and schizoaffective disorder were primarily illnesses. There were no psychologists at Charing Cross Hospital - I was just medicated and the doctors waited to see what effect it would have on me. To be honest in the first days I was there, I didn't want to go into the cognitive or psychoanalytical aspects of the illness anyway. People often think you should wheel in the psychologists straight away but I didn't want to talk about what had happened. I just wanted to forget about it and get back on my feet. Today, mental health professionals need to realise that psychosis is not just a biochemical or cognitive malfunction. They must understand that the roots of delusions and hallucinations are emotional and motivational. Some professionals in mental health don't seem to be very happy dealing with feelings and emotions. The emotional side of it is very disturbing to deal with and you need to time the treatment of this side of things properly. People try to find a one treatment catch-all approach and it's not helpful.

The mental health professionals who treated me successfully convinced me that I had had an illness. This made me realise that I had to treat what had happened to me very seriously. They gave me respect for the fact that there was a problem and I had to deal with it. However they didn't pick up on the fact that I had mild Tourette's syndrome which started at the same time as the delusions. The doctors didn't diagnose it but it was successfully treated by the haloperidol I was taking at the time. They just thought it was bottled up anger rather than a vocal tic. One psychotherapist told me to say the tics out loud which made it worse.

After I came out of hospital, the social workers at the psychiatric aftercare hostel were very strengthening because they fed me back a good image of myself. They taught me not to panic and stop feeling so guilty and ashamed. The treatment there included Gestalt therapy, encounter groups, meetings and reviews. I effectively did co-counselling with the other patients because I could talk to them about anything, which was very useful.

Transition towards recovery

I began to improve the moment the medication went into me. The effect was incredible, like being bounced out of a bad dream. The moment I woke up in my bed in Charing Cross Hospital, I recovered and was determined never to go back to psychosis or the person I was before. Psychosis had taken me under the wheels of a bus and I had a very unpleasant streak of callousness in my personality. My emotions of anger, fear and sexual arousal were on too high volume control and I had a very narrow attentional beam. The medication brought the volume of my emotions down, widened my attentional beam and took away the callousness. It made me less cynical and aggressive. The mentality I have while taking the medication seems more like what I was really like underneath all the macho training I got in Manchester and at home. It removed the barriers which were preventing me from being the person who I actually was and made me feel more like my real self than I was before. Before it was like I was walking around London in the blackout with a pencil torch. Ultimately, medication brought me back to sanity and I've maintained my sanity ever since. Before I took the medication I had what I refer to as the First Mind and afterwards the Second Mind. I have no intention of going back to the First Mind, so have never tried to come off the medication. People might say that I haven't recovered because I still take a small dose of medication. But I would say that isn't the point, because as far as I'm concerned, the problem is solved.

Getting back into work gave me a purpose which helped my recovery. It enabled me to develop a meaningful and fulfilling life. Thankfully the symptoms of my illness did not include hearing voices, because this would have prevented me from working so effectively over the past 30 years. I taught abnormal psychology at Birkbeck College for many years and always talked about my own experience to bring the material to life. I told my students about my own psychotic episode to illustrate psychological points, which they used to appreciate. It illustrated the point that all of these disorders are there within us all in seedling state. Over the years I wrote a lot about psychosis, including my book *Schizophrenia: The Positive Perspective* (1997), which helped me organise and clarify my thoughts. I've also written things against what I call 'the Masculinity and Heterosexuality Thought Police' which has been strengthening for me.

Making recovery a reality

I started looking at my recovery seriously five years after the illness when I felt a lot stronger. Rather like an electrical storm in my head, it had to subside before I could think more clearly. Firstly I thought about psychosis in a physical way, purely as a brain malfunction that could be solved by medication. I accepted that I had an illness and there was something organically wrong with my brain at the time I was psychotic. Then I considered it from a cognitive perspective. Getting onto the second PhD programme to read psychology helped me to do this. I specialised in psychosis and my thesis was entitled *A Psychological Study of Paranoia and Delusional Thinking*. I did a lot of experimental work on 'confirmation bias', which is where you are always looking for ways to confirm and sustain your beliefs. You don't notice things which might discredit or refute them. Delusions that are experienced during psychosis create confirmation bias towards the negative. So to avoid it, you have got to be careful of jumping to spectacular conclusions when something happens. You need to remember good things in the past, and avoid only retrieving negative autobiographical memories.

Once I had considered psychosis from a cognitive perspective, I looked at it psychoanalytically which was very disturbing to me. The effects were so tumultuous and volatile at first that I had to take extra medication, but they lessened as the years went by. These psychoanalytical ideas included the self-hatred and inadequacy you can have if you are not a 'real man'. I was brought up to be a self hating person and to be ashamed of myself. Psychoanalysis was particularly helpful for understanding why I was made to feel worthless by not fitting the typical 'Manchester man' model of what I should be. The men were so easily angered and aggressive but I didn't want to be that at all. I had to rewrite the narrative on myself because I'm a very different type of male person. I learned to understand myself as a placid, feminine man which is frankly not an easy identity to accept.

As the years went by, I began to consider the psychological stresses I was under at the time. I now see my illness as very political and think I was a victim of sex and gender fascism. The Masculinity and Heterosexuality Thought Police were trying to mould me into an army or football terraces man. I wasn't anything like that and the stress of it all destabilised my brain.

My spiritual life was very crass in those days and I had a very savage idea of God. I'd been brought up in the Christian religion and did sometimes go and sit in church to be at one with God and be peaceful. But my attitude to Him was wrong as I saw Him as a punishing entity. Spiritual issues became increasingly important to my recovery over the years. After the suicide attempt I began to realise that there must be some point to my existence or He would have allowed me to kill myself.

There are certain other things which have helped my recovery which I've ring-fenced and wouldn't necessarily apply to other people. One of these is a story told by a friend of mine. He was a rock climber and told me about this occasion when he was about 50 feet up this rock face and came off. He fell back and banged his head. The other climbers just stood there looking at him and the look on his friends faces seemed to say, "Don't just lie there, get up!" I never forgot this and used to think about it after the illness. If a psychiatric social worker had applied that to me, I wouldn't have liked it, but this was my attitude in my own head. I also modified Oscar Wilde's famous phrase to say, "For a psychologist to have one psychotic episode is unfortunate, but to have two psychotic episodes sounds like carelessness." I know there are other psychologists who have had multiple episodes and it wouldn't be fair to apply it to them because their circumstances are different. But I ring-fence this for myself and it helps me to stay stable.

Hope

Before I believed in God there was no hope or use to my life whatsoever. I'm 64 now and my main purpose these days is to get closer to Him. I'm concerned with being peaceful and my main interest is spirituality, which you can become alienated from if you are trained in science.

Having relationships with people who I can talk to about anything and everything has been very important. The most positive thing to come out of psychosis is an enhancement of my creativity. Creativity has given meaning to my life and I've lived on this since the episode. Writing, which is basically an artistic therapy, has been very valuable to me. But I'm frustrated that I can't seem to release the poet within, which is a part of me that is all concreted over with north of England tough talk and common sense.

Reflection

Psychosis has taught me the importance of consideration for other people and not living just to feel good all the time. Mental illness is a very narcissistic and solipsistic experience where you are the centre of the world. When you are well again, you're not so egocentric. I've always tried to relate my experience to universal concerns, which is useful in recovery because you become relevant to other people and not just wrapped up in yourself.

Not only do other people stigmatise people with psychosis, but people with psychosis also stigmatise themselves. Stigma and self-stigma can prevent recovery. People who have been psychotic have got to get away from seeing themselves as somehow categorically different to the rest of humanity or a failure. They need to realise there are many positive things about the tendency towards psychosis like creativity, sensitivity, spirituality and empathy. These are all advantages which they can put to use in life if they choose and believe in themselves. Recovering the positive things in life and organising your thoughts can get you back on the road to living in a fulfilling way. If you've hit the bottom, the rest of your life can only go up. The important thing is to be prepared to see psychosis as a multifaceted diamond, not just a biochemical or cognitive problem. If you see it as having many dimensions which takes a life process to get out of, you shouldn't be disheartened if you have any blips. Keep going and be prepared to use non-cognitive techniques if these are helpful.

In the 1970s and 1980s the main focus of treating mental illness was removal of the symptoms of delusions and hallucinations. If you could do that, the treatment was considered a success. Over the past two decades this has changed and we are now rather more concerned that the person has a quality of life and degree of fulfilment. Even if they still have some hallucinations and delusions, they can still have a meaningful life which gives them some happiness. New innovations in recovery such as sport and exercise psychology, and delusion and hearing voices support groups are very good. The energy of the service user movement is much to be praised though some people can be very anti-medication. A small dose of medication has actually helped me. My clarity of mind and organisation of thoughts were so increased that psychological techniques were more effective. The intensity and volatility of my emotions decreased so it became more possible to deal with them and feel the feelings, whereas before the feelings were so intense that they derailed me. While the medication does the basic job of removing or ameliorating the symptoms, more psychological and even spiritual interventions in the treatment of psychosis are needed.

There also needs to be more service user research and greater attention paid to the single case study, rather than large scale investigations. When you study the individual person they give out hints and strategies of how to get better which you can't always get from nomothetic research that uses large samples and gets average findings. It is also important to record narratives of individual people to see what their story is and what has helped them recover. There is a negative attitude to this which is to the detriment of mental health. Two reviewers criticised the inclusion of single case studies in my book *Schizophrenia: The Positive Perspective*. But the individual narrative blends contextually and the person's life as a totality feeds into how they got ill and got better.

Conclusion

Biological, cognitive, societal and political influences were all important in my becoming psychotic. My recovery from psychosis is a holistic discourse which goes from the biochemical right through to the spiritual and political. In many ways it's been a trip towards self-actualisation, of which the transvestism was also a part. There are so many ways that people can benefit from what happened to me and what I've written. As far as I'm concerned I am now cured and have lived a productive and reasonably successful life. Psychosis is not the end of the world. It can be the beginning of something once the worst of it is over, because in a way you have a new life afterwards. It's up to you to make out of it what you can.

Reference

Chadwick P K (1997) *Schizophrenia: The Positive Perspective*. Routledge: London.

Reaching Great Heights of Recovery

Chapter 17

Reaching Great Heights of Recovery

Stuart Baker-Brown, 45, from Bournemouth, Dorset, was told by a psychiatrist that he had one of the worst cases of undiagnosed schizophrenia ever seen. He refused to be written off and fought his way to recovery through determination and the correct medication. Stuart has since climbed to Everest Base Camp to promote positive recovery from schizophrenia and is an award-winning campaigner against mental health discrimination.

Background

Things started going wrong from a very early age for me. As a young kid and all through my teenage years, I wasn't functioning like other children. I can recognise being depressed from the age of five. At school I was very disruptive and treated as a naughty kid, but this was because I was frustrated. I couldn't comprehend what was being taught and it was like no one was speaking my language. Physically I was very fit though. My father was the national Olympic judo coach so I practised judo from the age of five. This sporting background opened doors for me and I joined the Royal Marines when I left school at the age of 16. I could cope with the physical side of training but not the mental pressure, like being woken up at 2am in the morning to go on ten mile runs. Part of the reason I wanted to go into the Marines was to escape a difficult family life. I had a very hard time with my parents who were constantly telling me I was failing and no good. This put a chip on my shoulder and I thought everybody viewed me in that way. My mother came from a very Victorian background where mental illness was viewed as a weakness. I can remember as a kid telling her I was depressed but she said that depression was for selfish people. By joining the Marines, I had gone from one bullying situation to another. I felt like an outcast, probably had depression and experienced some level of paranoia. After four months I left and came home to my family, going from job to job on building sites and farms. When I was 18 my family moved from Essex to Devon but I didn't feel part of society or like I belonged. The first possible signs of schizophrenia had begun to emerge because I felt very depressed and anxious at that time.

Transition towards illness

In 1991 there was suddenly an explosion in my mind and everything rose to the surface. I was on holiday in Moscow during the Soviet coup when members of the Communist Government tried to take control of the country from President Mikhail Gorbachev. There were very few other tourists there at the time as they had been given the option to get out of the city due to the political situation, but I decided to stay. I had a fascination with Russia so wanted to get involved, more because of the history of the occasion than due to any political beliefs. So I joined the protest marches against Communism that were happening on the streets. One night at about 2am I got a phone call in my hotel room. I understood a bit of Russian at the time and it was a man swearing at me because of my involvement in the marching. I never found out who it was but it triggered off great paranoia and unease in me. On my return to London, I started to feel that the Secret Services were out to harm me because I was a foreigner involving myself in Russian politics. I began to think that my life was under threat from the KGB. Many other people think it was possible that I *was* actually being followed at this time. One woman I met who used to work in Moscow for the British Embassy told me my experiences were typical of the tactics used by the KGB. But psychiatrists just put it all down to delusions and paranoia so it was very confusing for me to know who to believe. Now I think that there was probably something going on, but I don't believe my life was under threat. If anybody was following me, they just wanted to know who I was and what I was doing.

Realisation of problem

Within two or three weeks after returning from Moscow I was in a state. The sheer anxiety and stress I was under triggered paranoia, depression and psychosis. It hit me like a brick wall and within a few weeks I couldn't work and had become housebound. I was scared of everything and thought that everybody was linked to the Secret Services. Just walking to work, if somebody was looking at me I would associate them with the KGB. As I had a difficult home life, I couldn't even open up to my family because I thought they would be involved in harming me. I wanted to go to the police but thought they would be caught up in it too. At the time I was living and working in London, and forced myself to go and see a GP who signed me off from work straight away. Eventually I moved to a house on the edge of Exmoor in Devon where I thought the Secret Services wouldn't find me. I continued to see a GP in Devon who treated me for anxiety and depression. Although schizophrenia was suggested, it was not diagnosed. I was offered electro convulsive therapy on a few occasions and asked if I would enter into a psychiatric unit on a voluntary basis, but I refused. In 1996, I moved from Devon to Dorset where I was diagnosed as having paranoid schizophrenia and put on antipsychotic medication straightaway. My psychiatrist and psychiatric nurse both told me that I was one of the severest cases of undiagnosed schizophrenia they had ever come across. But I have never been treated in a psychiatric hospital because I fear the places and don't think they are the best places for people with mental illness. Plus I've never played about with my medication and always complied with whatever I've needed to recover. It took many years for me to get onto the correct one and I take quetiapine (Seroquel) now which works very well for me. Before that I was on risperidone (Risperdal) and it nearly killed me. I put on a huge amount of weight, going from a fit 14 stone to nearly 25 stone, and was diagnosed with type 2 diabetes as a result. Other horrible side effects included nightmares, shaking and memory loss, but I was just told that this was schizophrenia. It took nearly a year of fighting the psychiatric services to get my medication changed and it was only when my GP contacted them and said I was en route to a heart attack that they finally decided to do it. Within three weeks of being on quetiapine (Seroquel) all these disastrous side effects disappeared so they weren't the result of schizophrenia as I'd been led to believe. Although the new medication made me very sedated, I also started to feel better mentally. I felt brighter and more in control of my head. My health improved as I lost all the weight and became very fit. If I was back on risperidone, I think it would have harmed me greatly by now.

When I was first diagnosed, I read a leaflet from the mental health charity Rethink at my GP's surgery about schizophrenia with a list of the symptoms and I could tick all the boxes. In a way it was like I'd finally met with my enemy so I accepted the diagnosis straightaway. But what devastated me was the psychiatric view of schizophrenia and its response to my diagnosis. I was told by a psychiatrist and psychiatric nurse that I had to accept it was likely that I would never recover, never work again in my life and be treated as a potential threat to society. I remember asking my psychiatric nurse how they could say that, but he just told me that it was the way they had to view the diagnosis. It was like the day before I was diagnosed I was Stuart Baker-Brown and the day after I was somebody else I didn't know.

Now I don't experience any day-to-day symptoms of schizophrenia that I had in the past. The last time I experienced any was eight months ago, when I was walking down the High Street in Hertfordshire where I was living. I was looking at the sign for a Costa Coffee shop and saw it as the green Starbucks logo. I thought the shop had changed from Costa Coffee to Starbucks overnight, and then saw the sign change back to Costa Coffee before me. Things like that are intriguing, rather than frightening though it can sometimes cause a bit of confusion. But it's all I experience now, which doesn't bother me at all. I know I have recovered because I'm not in any emotional turmoil. I feel very inspired and enthusiastic about life and just want to continue going up and up in my recovery. There is nothing about schizophrenia that is holding me back apart from the stigma and discrimination towards my condition. But where the condition itself is concerned, I have no boundaries.

Contact with mental health professionals

The only mental health professional that has truly helped me was my former GP in Dorset who got the psychiatric services to change my medication. He was very caring towards me, showing empathy and compassion. In my own experience, the people in psychiatry who were there to help me have been the people that stigmatised and discriminated against me more than anybody. Psychiatric nurses and psychiatrists have hindered my progress because of their negative views towards me. I can't say anything about psychologists because I don't have any experience of them but psychiatrists have done nothing for me except write me off. I've felt more policed than cared for by psychiatry. I wanted to go back to work but was stopped when I was diagnosed which felt like they had taken my life away. The only way I truly started to recover was when I stepped away from the psychiatric services. I became me again and not the false identity that had been forced upon me.

A far more positive, compassionate and empathetic approach is needed for working with people with psychosis. Rather than just saying I was on the scrapheap of life and wasn't going to get anywhere, the mental health professionals should have been far more positive about the condition. Now everything I do is based on trying to change this negative attitude I've faced from day one of my diagnosis. There has got to be far more communication on an equal level because the experiences of people like me are not listened to enough. The sufferer needs to be treated as an individual and not as a diagnosis. The professionals should treat our own experience of psychosis as a reality and should not write off any unusual experience as mental illness and delusional - that causes far more confusion. Psychosis has taught me reality is an individual experience and no matter how weird that experience is, it is real to the individual who experienced it. I believe psychology needs to become much more involved with the treatment of psychosis, as psychology is more focused on understanding the mind's potential and its behaviour than psychiatry

Transition towards recovery

At the beginning of my illness, I wasn't aware that recovery from schizophrenia was a possibility so had to teach myself. For years I was desperate to find somebody in the media who had recovered but there was no one. Luckily enough the film *A Beautiful Mind* came along about the Nobel prize-winning mathematician John Nash. Seeing this film and reading his autobiography inspired me because many of his experiences were the same as mine. He also experienced paranoia and the feeling that he was being followed by the Secret Services, like me. This was the only person with schizophrenia I could find who had achieved so much yet would never recover. It was the one story I needed to hear and was a great inspiration to me.

The turning point in my recovery was me. I started to believe in myself and changed. I can remember sitting on the sofa one day when I was hugely overweight and thinking to myself, I'm either going to die or I'm going to fight this. So I chose to fight and became my own best healer. I accepted and really started to understand my diagnosis of schizophrenia. It didn't matter that I had a diagnosis - there was no reason why it should stop me from becoming who I knew I could become. Getting on the right medication was life changing and has helped me become the man I am today. I decided to try and work with the medication, trust it and gain insight into how it could help me improve.

A volunteer befriender from Rethink also helped me greatly in my recovery. I met him once or twice a week for a couple of years and he was the first person that told me I was a good man. Rather than being surrounded by people who told me I was wrong, I found someone who was totally on my level. I told him what my psychiatrist and psychiatric nurse had said about my never recovering, but he said that it was just their point of view. This befriender helped me change my thinking and agreed when I said I thought I could go on and achieve certain things. He was a very spiritual man and shared my beliefs about there being a potential link between psychic ability and psychosis. He helped me to believe in myself and that's when my recovery began.

Making recovery a reality

The meaning of recovery has changed for me over the years. At first it was about dealing with the symptoms but as life has progressed, it has become about living my life and achieving the things I want to do. Since I was a kid I'd wanted to visit Everest, so I applied for a Churchill Fellowship to trek to Everest Base Camp. The Fellowship is an award for travel that would make a positive difference and I wanted to use it to promote recovery from schizophrenia. Getting to Everest base camp would be very symbolic – reaching great heights was like what I'd done by overcoming schizophrenia. By undertaking the trek, I wanted to inspire others because I needed inspiring myself. People with psychosis need to believe that recovery is possible. I had to prove to the medical world, other people and myself that I could do it.

My bid was successful and I was awarded the Fellowship, so had to prepare for the trip. Getting out and training made me become well both emotionally and physically by not only helping me lose lots of weight, but really testing my symptoms of schizophrenia. Before I started training, I could hardly walk for more than ten minutes, but by the time I left for Kathmandu I was walking for four and a half hours a day up and down the hills of Dorset. Day after day I was fighting with paranoia but I mentally trained myself. When I was out walking alone in the woods, I'd hear a rustle behind a tree and thought it could be somebody coming to harm me. So I used to tell myself that I feared the same thing yesterday but nothing had happened. I was afraid of the KGB for many years and thought I was going to be killed, but taught myself to look at the reality of the situation in a very logical way. I reasoned with myself that the KGB had had plenty of chances to kill me and they hadn't done. The paranoia didn't change overnight and fighting it was very hard work, but I retrained my own mind to the reality that I had not come to any harm. I looked back at the times when I feared things and recognised that it was paranoia.

When I first arrived in Nepal, I was very excited and happy to be there. The psychosis still appeared in certain ways when I was very exhausted from a trek. I can remember lying on my bed and seeing in front of me all these amazing Buddhist images, like the tree of life. But it was very peaceful and not frightening at all. The trek was tough but I completed my goal of getting to Everest Base Camp and back within a month. I still had to fight stigma and discrimination all the way. I became quite unwell at altitude and a French doctor who checked up on me said that "someone like me" shouldn't be doing this type of thing. The psychiatric team back in Dorset assumed it was too much for someone with schizophrenia and that I would fail. But I didn't fail, I did it by believing in myself and understanding my capabilities. I recognised that the people around me were looking at schizophrenia, not Stuart Baker-Brown. But I thought, these people don't know me or my capabilities. Completing a trek to Everest Base Camp while on antipsychotic medication was a huge achievement, the scale of which became apparent when I got home. It made me realise that I could go on to do even greater things.

The Fellowship had funded my trip and I'd used part of the money to buy a camera. While I was away I took lots of photographs of Everest but didn't think much of them. When I got back, a journalist who came round to interview me about the trek saw them laid out on the table and said, "Wow!" She published them in her paper and started putting me in touch with galleries. Since then I've been successful in exhibiting my photography and it has even been seen by royalty.

I also got very involved in media work and campaigning on mental illness for Rethink. I've done interviews with Radio 4, Radio 5 and have written for the *British Medical Journal* and the BBC. I appeared in the short film *Schizo* which is part of the Time to Change campaign against mental health discrimination and can be found on their website. My media work was recognised when I won a *Third Sector* Award for Excellence. All this work has been motivated by trying to fight the kind of stigma and discrimination I've experienced from healthcare professionals, my family and society. By promoting understanding, acceptance and hope, I want to offer others who are experiencing mental illness the things that have kept me going.

Hope

Hope has been immense in my recovery and I've always tried to speak about it in the context of mental illness. Hopes and dreams are what have kept me going, but it doesn't really matter if they don't materialise. For many years I was hopeless because everyone around me was saying there was no hope of recovery. Psychiatry told me that I couldn't achieve all I would achieve. I've spoken about hope on international panels with world leaders in mental health and renowned psychiatrists and the answer I've always got from them is that they don't want to give false hope. That is terrible because everybody needs hope and it's devastating when apparent experts take it away from you. Mental health professionals need to promote recovery and offer hope to people who are experiencing mental illness as a priority.

My hope for the future is to get back into full time employment, but stigma and discrimination could stop me achieving that. I've written my CV and been assigned a special person at the Job Centre to help me find a job. But ironically I've been told that employers could be put off because of the campaigning work I have done against stigma! I also want to continue with my writing and travelling. I want to keep growing and take what I'm doing to even greater levels. I have a diagnosis of schizophrenia and live daily on antipsychotic medication yet it hasn't stopped me doing anything. Hopefully that will inspire people with psychosis and give them hope. They could recognise that if I can do it so can they, or better.

Reflection

When I was first diagnosed with schizophrenia I thought my life had ended and that the pain and destruction I was experiencing would stay with me forever. Hope and recovery were neither talked about nor offered. But now I recognise that people with psychosis can adapt and live successfully with it. I also believe that we know very little about the condition. I've dealt with psychiatrists for many years now and they have given me very few answers. All I know is that we don't have much understanding of psychosis at all. I also believe there is a lot about psychosis that is not down to mental illness. We know very little about the human mind and its capabilities. Some of the experiences I've had in the past I believe were due to psychic ability rather than mental illness. I put it down to possibly being psychic and believe there is a clear difference between psychic activity and psychosis, having experienced both. Psychiatry will not accept this but I believe there is truth in it and know these things go on. Psychiatrist RD Laing was outcast in the 1950s and 60s for his views on schizophrenia. He said that the mystic and the schizophrenic share the same ocean, where the mystic swims but the schizophrenic drowns. But in my view, some psychic ability is put down to mental illness when it shouldn't be.

Psychosis is a very creative condition that can be a wonderful experience. There have been many great thinkers, artists and scientists who have been linked to schizophrenia or psychotic-type symptoms. There was a recent BBC article written by a psychologist who said that there is very similar brain activity in the brains of people with schizophrenia and artists. In people like me, it will lead to mental illness but artists like Salvador Dalí will excel. Psychosis can be many things – it can be both a calming and terrifying experience. It can be a very beautiful thing.

Psychosis has definitely enhanced my creativity in life. I've always said to myself that something as destructive as schizophrenia must have a creative side. It's always been my determination to turn my experience of it into a positive, creative thing. Though psychosis can be both unique and devastating, I don't want to experience any of the devastation again. Now I have far more empathy and compassion towards those who suffer from mental illness. I really want to help them, and show them that it can be overcome.

Conclusion

Schizophrenia and psychosis has made me the man I am today. I wouldn't have trekked in the Himalayas to promote positive recovery from schizophrenia, wouldn't have won a Churchill Fellowship, or a *Third Sector* Award for Excellence for all the media work I've done, or had photographic exhibitions that have been viewed by royalty. Recently I talked about my schizophrenia in the Master's Lodge at St John's College, Cambridge. Without psychosis or schizophrenia, I wouldn't have done any of this. So I've turned round the devastation into creation. It's given me a focus, a meaning which is to help others. For many years before, I didn't have any meaning in life. I was lost and thought I was a no hoper because that's what I'd been told. Now I am fully focused in what I do. It's a part of me and has pushed me forward to a greater understanding of myself and others.

The Confidence Builder

Chapter 18

The Confidence Builder

John Lawrence, 43, from Clapham, South London, developed schizophrenia suddenly while working as a builder in his twenties and has been receiving treatment for over 20 years. His recovery has taken on a new dimension in the last two years due to finding the right medication and engaging positively with cognitive behaviour therapy.

Background

As I was born in Balham and have lived in Lambeth or Wandsworth for most of my life, I'd class myself as a true South Londoner. At school I was the class clown and was always trying to make people laugh. I suppose I was a bit of a bad boy and got suspended a few times. At one point, the deputy head said I should see a child psychologist so I don't know if he'd seen something in me that would later develop into mental illness. Now when I look back at my time at school, I wish I'd knuckled down a bit more. When I left school I went straight into a job on a building site, just a couple of days after my sixteenth birthday. It was mainly offices and hospitals that I was building, and I worked on the British Library. Even at work I used to mess around a bit, getting sacked and reinstated a few times over the years. It was the 1980s, I was going into my early twenties and just wanted to enjoy myself. I used to go nightclubbing all over London, and bought myself nice clothes and a new car. As I worked on building sites, I was physically strong and assumed I was mentally strong too. But as a young man, the stresses and strains of life sometimes played a part. I did some silly things from time to time, taking the odd funny cigarette and drinking quite heavily. It was just recreational stuff and I have no time for people that take drugs now. But it could have been a catalyst for me getting ill with schizophrenia at the age of 21.

Transition towards illness

The first symptoms happened on Christmas Day in 1988. I was in a pub with a group of friends when it felt like my head was exploding and I just fell to my knees. The feeling came completely out of the blue and I'd never experienced anything like it before in my life. I had no notion of mental illness and there's none in my family, so I didn't know what was happening to me. My friends and girlfriend helped me to my feet and I managed to get home. I was a bit concerned so went to see my GP who prescribed me antidepressants and put me under the care of a psychiatrist at King's College Hospital. In the latter half of 1989 things progressed back to normal - I felt better and was working. Then in the summer of 1990, things started to go wrong with my feelings and thoughts. At the time I was living in a bedsit in Tooting and working on a building site in Chatham, Kent. I was hearing voices and thought that people were laughing at me. There's a lot of jovial banter and Mickey-taking on building sites and I started getting a bit aggressive and stressed out at work. Then one day, it got so bad that I ran next door to my neighbours because I thought they were talking about me. I was so panicked that I ran all the way from Tooting to my parent's flat in Norwood. Normally I wouldn't run that far even if I was a jogger, but I thought someone was shooting at me. I was totally confused, disorientated and hallucinating. I thought I heard bullets bouncing off the pavement and that SAS snipers were after me. When I look back it seems funny, but at the time it was very scary. I suppose these are the sort of things you go through in the process of becoming a schizophrenic. When I got to my parents they took me to the Maudsley Hospital where I saw a doctor as an emergency. There was a helicopter flying over the hospital and I thought people were abseiling down from it to come and get me. In hospital, I was assessed and put under Section for 28 days as they thought I was too ill to go back onto the streets. Two nurses took me off to Dulwich Hospital in a cab. This was in August and I didn't come out until April the following year. While in hospital I was diagnosed with paranoid schizophrenia but this didn't make much of an impression on me as I wasn't in any fit state to understand what was going on.

Realisation of problem

Once at Dulwich Hospital, I was terrified as I didn't know what to expect. I didn't know what the other patients were going to be like and had heard stories about people getting beaten up. The whole experience was devastatingly scary at first because I was hearing voices all the time and thought I was never going to get better. At that stage of my illness, everything I thought and heard was about people trying to harm me. But the treatment was very good and I never experienced any violence myself. I kept pestering my family, forever ringing them up to come and get me out of hospital. I was a grown man acting like a child. In the early stages the doctors tried me out on different medication, first giving me chlorpromazine then haloperidol. I was on haloperidol for about ten years, but would get "stary turns" where I couldn't have any eye contact with people. If I was out on the street, I would panic and have to get home. I think they changed my medication because each drug had run its course. If the medication you're on isn't good enough and you get too used to it, the symptoms start to come back. Everybody gets a bit down from time to time, but if you have got mental illness you begin to think, "Oh no, is it going to happen again?"

While working in Staines in 1996, I fell ill again with hearing voices and paranoia. At the time, I was feeling very stressed out and had been drinking. I ran into a hospital in Ashford and told them I suffered from psychiatric problems. It was freezing and snowing at the time and all I wanted to do was fall over and die there and then. I thought no one would miss me and the cold would kill me. I flagged someone down at a petrol station and got them to give me a lift back to the building site in Staines. When I got there, I just burst into tears and said I needed someone to try and get me home. Luckily enough a work colleague gave me a lift back to my doorstep in Clapham.

Crisis points

In total I've spent about 15 months in hospital including two long stays in Dulwich then Lambeth Hospitals under Section. While I was in Lambeth in 2004, I was very ill because they put me on a drug which didn't suit me. This made me do things that were out of character like stripping off, going out into the gardens and lying in the shape of a star. At no time in my illness had I gone completely naked before and I was very embarrassed about it. I remember it vaguely but choose to forget. A girlfriend had come to visit me and could see I wasn't well. She asked the doctors what medication they had given me and told them that it was wrong if it make me act that way. They didn't know what medication to put me on and at one stage thought I had petit mal which is a minor form of epilepsy. I was given tablets to take for this which were the size of bullets. For eight months I suffered like this and the voices got worse and worse. I'd come out of hospital in September but by Christmas the voices had become so bad that I took an overdose of my medication. I couldn't put up with the voices any more. It was like I had an angel on one shoulder and a devil on the other. They voices were either against me or commanding me to do things that I didn't want to do, like attack people. I had also become very paranoid. Every time I went out of my flat I thought people were after me. I'd never felt so alone in my life but people couldn't understand how I felt. I didn't want to die; I just wanted a way out.

Contact with services and treatment

The overdose was the lowest point I'd reached as before that I'd always conquered any suicidal thoughts. But I was just trying to get rid of all the voices. When I took the overdose, my girlfriend phoned the home treatment team from Lambeth Hospital who were with me straight away in the early hours of the morning and rang an ambulance. They came to King's College Hospital with me and I was able to go home for New Year's Day. Later the home treatment team and my girlfriend helped me by encouraging me to go back into hospital voluntarily and try a different medication. My girlfriend got on her knees and begged me to go back, as I wouldn't go anywhere near a psychiatric hospital unless under Section, let alone voluntarily. But I knew I had to do something to deal with the voices, so I went back into hospital and was put on clozapine. That's when everything started to improve. Today I don't suffer any symptoms of schizophrenia like hearing voices, though I can get a bit paranoid when I hear a noise or comment. But now I nip these thoughts in the bud and switch off straight away.

Contact with mental health professionals

The home treatment team from Lambeth Hospital were a God-send for me. The team is a relatively new service where they treat you at home so you don't have to be Sectioned or go into hospital voluntarily. You can ring them 24 hours a day if you are panicking or hearing voices. After the suicide attempt, I was not given my own supply of medication, so someone from the team used to have come around and give it to me every day. That went on until they could trust me to manage my own medication again, which I have been doing to this day. Not to blow my own trumpet but I was a success story in their eyes. While in hospital, I'd gone down to about 11 stone because I wasn't eating properly but when I saw one of the team in a supermarket the other day, he couldn't believe how well I looked. One psychiatric nurse who was part of the home treatment team got to know me and my girlfriend very well. When I was really ill, I wouldn't go out so sometimes she would take me for a drive in her car. She would even come onto the ward I was on to see how I was, even though it wasn't part of her job. We had a bit of a bond and she went the extra mile for me. When I was being treated at a community mental health team in Brixton, I would regularly see a psychiatric nurse who was very nice. We would go out for a walk or she'd talk to me and put me at ease, just like a friend. She'd tell me it would be OK and try to get me to do things with my time that would help me get better.

Psychiatrists are good although I see a different one every six months. At one stage I had a regular psychiatrist who was very nice. But when you have to see someone new every six months, you end up going over everything each time and there's lack of consistency. When you have been ill for 20 years you don't want to keep going back over the past. I tell the psychiatrists things that they should already know if they look at their notes. I think psychologists are better than psychiatrists. Psychiatrists help you with diagnostics and medication but psychologists gives you the tools you need to get on with your everyday life. The cognitive behavioural therapy (CBT) and recovery work I have done with my clinical psychologist has been brilliant. I can be thinking negatively but come along to CBT and he will put a positive spin on things. Regardless of whether it is what I want to hear, he will come back with an honest answer. This makes me think, he's right, why didn't I think of that? I am very relaxed with my psychologist and can tell him anything. I was offered CBT years ago but didn't know what it entailed and wasn't in the right state of mind. Perhaps the times I've spent under Section in hospital could have been avoided if I'd seen a psychologist and had CBT earlier in my life. Maybe this new positivity that I've got would have happened ten or 15 years ago and I might not have had relapses in 1996 and 2004. But there is no point taking CBT until you are a certain point along the road in your recovery. You have to want to make it work for yourself.

Transition towards recovery

Your level of recovery depends on what brings on your schizophrenia in the first place. In my case, my psychiatrist and psychologist will tell you that stress makes my illness come back. If stress didn't affect me I would be working but I haven't had proper employment since I got ill in 1996. A few years ago I took a computer course to try and better myself. I was doing well and got a certificate but couldn't sit the exam. It felt like my head was going to explode again, like back in 1988. But I am keen to get a job as I miss the regularity of getting up, going to work on the building sites and an income. An occupational therapist at a community mental health team I attended referred me to see someone who tried to get me employment. But during the sessions I started to get stressed so I said I couldn't go along any more. It will be difficult to find a job that isn't stressful. I need to find something like being a postman, where I can be on my own, which gets me outside and where I'm my own boss. Apparently four out of ten employers won't hire someone with mental illness but I don't want to lie to my employers. I might not experience another episode of schizophrenia in my life but in the eyes of the law and the medical profession, I am a schizophrenic and have to live with it. It has taken me 16 years to get to the stage where I can identify if any symptoms are coming on and the situations to avoid. Maybe with this new medication I could take a bit more stress than I was comfortable with before.

Making recovery a reality

The right medication is one of the factors that have helped me get to this stage of recovery. I don't think my recovery could be elevated any higher unless there was some miracle that took the stress factor away. I went onto clozapine in 2005 which is in my eyes the best medication I've ever taken.

It's helped me no end in the five years I've been taking it and has stopped me hearing voices. At first it was a struggle because it gave me involuntary body jerks, but I got used to it. Changing aspects of my life also helped me start to improve. My psychiatrist referred me for CBT which I've now been having for two years. This helped me develop more positive ways of thinking and has grown my confidence. Years ago, if I was offered something like CBT I would have said it wasn't for me and that someone else who needed it more than me should go instead. But now if I'm offered something that might help with my recovery, I think about saying 'yes' first. It's braver to say yes and go ahead than not to do it.

Now if my psychologist asks me to take part in something I will do it. I take part in things I previously wouldn't have done. I came to all ten recovery workshops run by my psychologist and thoroughly enjoyed them all. I've even been to a poetry session with quite a few other service users. Normally I wouldn't read poetry, let alone turn up and listen to it, but it was good. My family and girlfriend said I would have never done anything like that years ago. I'm a Liverpool FC supporter and was recently taken up to Anfield on my birthday for a few nights. On the guided tour I stood up and started asking questions in front of about 70 adults. Normally I get nervous just speaking on the telephone so I was quite impressed with myself for doing this!

I see things differently now and am starting to live a more fulfilling life. I get out and about visiting places on a regular basis. I try to keep fit - the clozapine can make you put on weight but I try to walk 45 minutes every day. I stay in at night and don't drink much alcohol any more like I used to. I was also a born worrier but now I cross each bridge as I come to it. Someone once said to me if you are worrying about something in your life, you're not going to live your life. Now I believe we're not here long enough to worry.

Having good relationships is vital to recovery. My family has helped me so much with my illness and would visit me regularly in hospital. I've got lots of friends from different periods of my life and they have been very helpful. They are always asking me how I am and there is no negativity towards me even though they know I have got schizophrenia. My girlfriend has also been brilliant during my illness. There aren't many people who could handle being with someone who has schizophrenia but she was well aware of it before we started going out together. She's always there when I need her and I can tell her anything. I would recommend a relationship to anyone because if you are on your own you can get down and depressed, resorting back to your old life of drinking or smoking drugs.

Looking after your appearance can help you feel more confident. If you feel confident, you can go a long way in your recovery. When you are mentally ill you tend not to look after yourself as much as you should. I lost a lot of teeth in hospital because I didn't clean them properly and was eating sweets, but this could have been avoided. Keeping yourself clean and wearing clean clothes doesn't take a lot of effort. If you feel good in yourself and like the clothes you have got on, you will feel ten foot tall.

Hope

I've got plenty of hope for the future. My intention is to stay out of hospital and continue to recover from schizophrenia. I hope to stay in my relationship and that my family remains well. I want to carry on with the activities I'm involved in now and visit more places in the UK. Hopefully I'll go to Ireland later this year and try and have a holiday next year. I look forward to the football season starting, the summer and my birthday. Eventually I hope to get an everyday job like I used to.

I can offer hope to people with schizophrenia by saying that it does get better over time. You have to change your life to adapt to the illness otherwise you will just spend your life in a psychiatric hospital or medicated up to the eyeballs. But if you have a healthy life and learn to live with your illness, you will come through it and get over it. My advice is to accept certain services if they are offered to you, such as a community psychiatric nurse, a home treatment team or CBT. Unless you try them, you don't know if they are going to work. If you make an effort, you could be surprised at how much better you will get and how your life could change. I would also advise a person with schizophrenia to comply with their medication and make sure whatever they are given is right for them. If you are not sure what medication you are on, make sure a member of your family does, including any side effects and whether you are able to drink alcohol. Don't take illegal substances, as these will only make the illness worse. They will stop the medication working properly and the psychiatrist won't know what's going on in your head. They can only get feedback from what you tell them. If you don't tell them how you're feeling, they can't help you. You have to be honest with them otherwise you are just wasting each other's time.

Reflection

When you use the big S word – schizophrenia – the first impression people have is that you're a madman. But the truth is that schizophrenics are often more scared of other people than scary themselves. I was petrified in the early stages and felt like an outcast. But you can create that stigma for yourself. For the first five or ten years of my illness, I would tell people I wasn't doing anything with my life because I was schizophrenic. But now I don't tell them anything about my illness and to look at me you wouldn't think there was anything wrong. They can't see into my head or see what's wrong with me so they can't judge me.

I don't think there's as much stigma surrounding schizophrenia as there used to be. But I don't like how every time a crime is committed by a mental patient, it's blown out of all proportion by the newspapers. When people who are ill commit a crime it's not them doing it. It's the voices inside that make them angry because they can't cope with it and lash out at somebody. The most positive thing you can do to the voices is not listen to them because what they are saying is not true. It's just voices that can't harm you.

Conclusion
When I first got ill with schizophrenia I thought my life was over, but I knew I had to fight it. This fight has taken 20 years of hard struggle, but it was either that or spend 20 years in a psychiatric unit. Now I think schizophrenia was one of the best things that ever happened to me because it has helped me get to know myself better. There are so many different emotions you go through and it's so frightening but you learn to deal with it. I've been at the brink of the abyss but have come back two or three times. There are people out there a lot worse off than me. I could have been an alcoholic or sleeping out on the streets, which would have been a lot worse than a mental health problem. When you are physically or mentally disabled yourself your attitude changes. It's made me more compassionate and I have learned that you should never mock someone less fortunate than yourself. Your priorities change too. People moan about becoming bankrupt but I feel like saying go and spend six months in a psychiatric hospital then you won't worry about money. Recovery from schizophrenia is possible but don't just take a leaf out of my book. Take a leaf out of this book. There are 14 characters with individual stories and reading other people's experience of recovery will help your own.

Chapter 19

Afterword: The Value of Recovery Stories

By Hannah Cordle, Frank Holloway and Jerome Carson

This book contains recovery stories from 14 people who have received a diagnosis of psychosis. These stories, if nothing else, confirm that people who live with this diagnosis can, and do, live full and important lives – a proposition that is both obviously true (to those who live with mental illness and their carers) and surprising (to the general public, who receive relentlessly negative messages about psychosis).

Readers will immediately see that these stories are very individual and reflect the specific personal journeys that our contributors have undergone. One very clear message from this book is that a diagnosis of psychosis tells us no more about the person who receives this diagnosis than it would about someone with a diagnosis of, for example, diabetes or breast cancer. However we must be clear that individuals living with psychosis, diabetes or breast cancer all have problems that potentially require treatment and support.

The book began by describing how the stories were recorded. Dr Frank Holloway has tried to set out the current professional understanding of what psychosis means. Dr Jerome Carson has provided an account of attempts to define recovery within the context of mental health services. Dr Glenn Roberts makes a very powerful statement about the importance of stories for people in making sense of and overcoming the experience of severe mental illness.

Despite the very clear individuality of the recovery stories described in this book some themes do emerge. These themes can readily be organised under the four key components of Recovery described by Retta Andresen and colleagues (Andresen et al, 2003).

- **Restoration of hope**

- **Development of a positive sense of identity**

- **Having a life that is more meaningful**

- **Taking more of a sense of responsibility for one's life**

The narratives in this book give some answers as to how each of these components can be achieved. Here we quote directly from the stories of our contributors.

Restoration of hope

Being told by someone in a position of authority (such as a clinician) that recovery is possible can give hope.

> *"I've been ill for 20 years but nobody told me recovery was possible until I started working with my psychologist,"* (Esther Maxwell-Orumbie).

> *"[My psychiatric nurse] said there was no reason why I shouldn't [travel to America] because I seemed quite recovered, as long as I kept taking my medication,"* (Helen George).

> *"I didn't think recovery was possible until I started having therapy with my psychologist and attending his workshops,"* (Michelle McNary).

> *"I came to all ten recovery workshops held by my psychologist,"* (John Lawrence).

> *"My occupational therapist asked me how I was and how were the voices. I told her they were there, but not too aggressive. She said I had just turned a corner in my life,"* (Peter Bullimore).

> *"[My psychologist] informed me that recovery from mental illness was a possibility when I never thought it was before,"* (James Bellamy).

However being told by an authority figure that recovery is not possible can remove hope.

> *"I was told by a psychiatrist and psychiatric nurse that I had to accept it was likely that I would never recover, never work again in my life and be treated as a potential threat to society...[I have talked to] world leaders in mental health and renowned psychiatrists and the answer I've always got from them is that they don't want to give false hope,"* (Stuart Baker-Brown).

> *"[I] remember the consultant psychiatrist's words, 'Mr Bullimore, you are a chronic schizophrenic and you will never, ever work again. Go away and enjoy your life,'"* (Peter Bullimore).

Pursuing personal goals or dreams can foster hope.

> *"One great hope is that I can register this social enterprise so we could do the kind of the projects that I know of in London...here in Sussex,"* (Andrew Voyce).

> *"My occupational therapist found me the opportunity to have a solo exhibition at the Bethlem Royal Hospital art gallery in Beckenham last November... Hopefully I'll be having another exhibition at the Bethlem Gallery in a few years time,"* (Ben Haydon).

> *"The next film I hope to produce is called Climbing Walls, about a young woman who is suffering from psychosis and how her family responds,"* (Michelle McNary).

> *"My dream is to restart the [music] project as an after school music clubs to teach children the music they want to do on an informal basis,"* (Carl Lee).

Finding the right medication can give hope.

> *"I began to improve the moment the medication went into me,"* (Peter Chadwick).

> *"Amisulpride has been like a wonder drug for me... After three years of taking it, I'm more well than I've ever been in my entire life,"* (Ben Haydon).

> *"The right medication is one of the factors that have helped me get to this stage of recovery,"* (John Lawrence).

Maintaining good personal relationships with family and friends can give hope.

> *"Meeting [my wife] Jill was a turning point... She was perfectly accepting of what had happened to me having had mental health problems herself,"* (Peter Chadwick).

> *"Having good relationships is vital to recovery...I would recommend a relationship to anyone because if you are on your own you can get down and depressed,"* (John Lawrence).

"[My partner] has really helped my recovery by teaching me how to communicate in a more effective way...My family has tried to encourage me," (Bose Dania).

"So I'm building up my circle of friends from way back in my school days," (Ben Haydon).

"[Domino] sessions and friends have helped my recovery a lot because they gave me regularity, sociality and distract me from living a schizophrenic life," (Gordon McManus).

Development of a positive sense of identity

Finishing education, getting job training or engaging in structured activities can be a major step to developing a sense of identity.

"The people at the local day centre that I've attended regularly over the past 20 years have been very helpful, particularly the manager who encouraged me to finish my degree," (Andrew Voyce).

"My psychiatric nurse came round once a week and I saw the psychiatrist every couple of months...During this time I managed to finish my MA and I'm really proud of that," (Helen George).

"I considered [my psychosis] from a cognitive perspective. Getting onto the second PhD programme to read psychology helped me to do this," (Peter Chadwick).

"The clinical psychologist I saw in hospital was absolutely fantastic and really took me under her wing. She convinced the university to accept me back again to re-sit my exams," (Emma Harding).

Self-advocacy through speaking about one's own illness or taking an active role with other service users provides another route to a positive identity.

"Advocates and self advocates like Survivors Speak Out and Survivors' Poetry started up...they encouraged...the writing down or painting or setting to poetry or music of narrative," (Andrew Voyce).

"[My occupational therapist] told me that the hearing voices group at Mind had closed and suggested I started another one," (Peter Bullimore).

"I taught a six week Introduction to Song Writing course which got the service users to be more self-expressive and exercise their creativity," (Carl Lee).

Sometimes, perhaps paradoxically, the illness itself can lead to a sense of purpose.

"The belief that I have a role to play in public and others people's lives has been hugely important in my recovery. It gives me a sense of purpose and proves I'm a relevant person, which weakens the illness," (James Bellamy).

"It made me realise I had a purpose in life and that my...purpose and destiny is to spread love and joy to the world through art," (Carl Lee).

"After the suicide attempt I began to realise that there must be some point to my existence or [God] would have allowed me to kill myself," (Peter Chadwick).

"Helping others is the icing on the cake for me, but when other people do well it also reinforces to me that recovery is possible," (Emma Harding).

Having a life that is more meaningful

People can use their own experience of mental illness to help others.

"All this work has been motivated by trying to fight the kind of stigma and discrimination I've experienced from healthcare professionals, my family and society," (Stuart Baker-Brown).

"Volunteering with Mind on mental health campaigns, I got to learn more about the issues and attended a reception at the House of Commons about women with mental illness in prison," (Bose Dania).

"When I thought I was God I thought I wanted to cure poverty and disease. I know I can't do that but I can use my experience of surviving psychosis to help other people find their way through," (Emma Harding).

"Hopefully people will learn from the mistakes I made, such as disengaging from the hearing voices group and trying to push the psychiatrist and occupational therapist away," (Peter Bullimore).

A meaningful life can come through the development of one's creativity and self-expression. This can come through writing and poetry (Peter Chadwick, Helen George, Gordon McManus, Bose Dania and James Bellamy), music (Carl Lee and Andrew Voyce), art (Esther Maxwell-Orumbie and Ben Haydon) or film and acting (Michelle McNary)

Developing spirituality or practising religion are highly significant for many people.

> *"Before I believed in God there was no hope or use to my life whatsoever. I'm 64 now and my main purpose these days is to get closer to Him,"* (Peter Chadwick).

> *"I'm a more secure person because I've sorted out my spirituality problems and know what I believe,"* (Helen George).

> *"A turning point for me was when I started to have a relationship with God or the Creator,"* (Carl Lee).

> *"Without my Christian faith I don't know what I would have done because it has given me an anchor,"* (Esther Maxwell-Orumbie).

Taking more of a sense of responsibility for one's life

Service user involvement in care and treatment is an important element in recovery for many people.

> *"We had things like user groups, a user charter and user democracy. This was the start of empowerment for me,"* (Andrew Voyce).

> *"Another doctor supported me if I wanted to reduce my medication,"* (Esther Maxwell-Orumbie).

> *"I developed a model of my own recovery process to help me structure and rationalise my illness,"* (Gordon McManus).

> *"I refused to be hospitalised so they said they'd give me a couple more days to take my medication and sort myself out…I regret that my only choice was to take the medication or go into hospital,"* (Helen George).

> *"I would visit my occupational therapist every week and have a therapy session. She would get me involved in various projects and therapeutic activities,"* (Ben Haydon).

Addressing and accepting the past can be helpful.

> *"I had certain issues which could have been dealt with. They could have applied for an aegrotat degree for me…they could have given me help to recover the sum of money which I'd put into the family firm…[I] would have been happy to tell the police all I knew about the drug scene,"* (Andrew Voyce).

"The mental health system disempowers people and I realised I needed to take the power back for myself. So I locked myself away and listened intently to what the voices were telling me," (Peter Bullimore).

"I would sit on my own pretending to be a counsellor, asking myself questions and answering them. These questions included what caused my illness and how could my childhood have affected it," (Bose Dania).

"When I was a child I was very badly bullied at primary school and think perhaps that could have caused this illness...I'd like to explore some of this so I could wash it away," (James Bellamy).

Some people describe the value of cutting out negative influences in one's life.

"I used to listen to electronic dance music on Kiss FM but it got tiresome and monotonous. So I discarded it...My life is so much better now I've got rid of the television," (Ben Haydon).

"I stay in at night and don't drink much alcohol any more like I used to," (John Lawrence).

"I try to stay stress-free and do the things that contribute towards my wellbeing," (Gordon McManus).

"I stopped smoking weed at around this time, which I'd been doing since I was 16 and my partner said he couldn't believe the difference in me," (Bose Dania).

Understanding of one's condition can be a vital tool in managing the illness.

"Everyone's symptoms are different but you need to be able to recognise the early signs so you can do something about it," (Bose Dania).

"The more I learn about my illness the better, because I become more aware of the dangers," (Helen George).

"If I begin to get some symptoms I know what I should be doing, such as slowing down, taking things easy and making sure I'm on the right dose of medication," (Esther Maxwell-Orumbie).

"There have been wobbly times when things got stressful but I've managed to keep it under control," (Emma Harding).

"It's a good thing when my voices get loud because they are my early warning signs," (Peter Bullimore).

People report various strategies for taking control of cognitive processes.

- Ignoring voices (eg John Lawrence and Gordon McManus)ï

- Positive thinking (eg Helen George and Esther Maxwell-Orumbie)

- Rationalising paranoia (eg Stuart Baker-Brown, Helen George and Esther

  Maxwell-Orumbie)

Finally, although almost all these stories reveal times where services were perceived as unhelpful, or even perhaps positively harmful, positive engagement with services is most certainly possible.

> *"Cooperating with your doctor is important,"* (Esther Maxwell-Orumbie)

> *"Get talking therapies if you need them and if you can...Get help, get an advocate and some idea of what self advocacy is available,"* (Andrew Voyce).

> *"You have to use the resources around you and not try and get through it alone,"* (Peter Bullimore).

> *But now if I'm offered something that might help with my recovery, I think about saying 'yes' first,"* (John Lawrence).

Concluding comments

All the contributors have a unique story to tell about living with psychosis. Each story describes very difficult times for an individual and a unique journey through and beyond those times. Although these stories are unique, taken together they give a powerful picture of what it is like to receive a diagnosis of psychosis, to be engaged with a mental health system that is often experienced as unhelpful and unnecessarily controlling, to live within a society that heavily stigmatises mental illness (particularly psychosis) and still after all this to be able to exercise control and live a meaningful life.

References

Andresen R, Oades L, Caputi P (2003) The experience of recovery from schizophrenia: Towards an empirically validated stage model. *Australian and New Zealand Journal of Psychiatry*, **37**, 5, 586-594